SEDIMENTOLOGY BOOK ❷

The Depositional Environments

Chris King

ISBN:0582085071
KING, CHRIS
GEOLOGY: SEDIMENTOLOGY. BOOK 2: THE DEPOSITIONA
CLASS :551.3   LOC/IDENT : A

The Author

CHRIS KING is Head of Geology at Altrincham Grammar School for Boys, where he also co-ordinates the teaching of Science in the lower school. He teaches A-level Geology to boys from this school and to girls from the nearby Altrincham Grammar School for Girls. He is currently Chairman of the Earth Science Teachers' Association, and has been Chairman of the Association's Curriculum Working Group. He is also a member of the Joint Matriculation Board A-level Geology committees. His practical experience of Sedimentology includes five years spent prospecting for diamonds in Africa and Australia.

ISBN 0 582 08507 1

First published 1991

© Longman Group UK Ltd

Set in 11 on 12 pt Times

Printed in Great Britain by Longman Group Resources Unit.

Contents

Acknowledgements

I would like to thank Peter Kennett and John McManus for their sterling work on commenting upon, and improving, early versions of the manuscript. Peter Kennett's encouragement throughout has been particularly valuable. Any errors remaining in the book are entirely my own.

I would also like to thank Helen Busteed for her careful drafting of the diagrams, and Keith Nodding, Headmaster of Altrincham Grammar School for Boys, for providing me with working facilities.

Finally, without the support of my wife and family, these books would not have been written and I thank them for their continuing encouragement.

Chris King

Preface

This book has been designed, together with its companion book *Sedimentology Book 1*, *Processes and Analysis*, to provide all the material necessary for the study of Sedimentology at sixth-form level, and to provide useful background material for college and university students beginning courses in Geology or Earth Science.

The two books cover all the core topics relating to surface processes and sedimentary rocks that are contained in existing A- and AS-level Geology syllabuses. This material will also be of value in the teaching of those aspects of Sedimentology and related topics that are expected to appear in the sixth-form Earth Science courses of the near future. In addition, those studying Physical Geography will find many sections of the books helpful.

Also covered are many of the economic aspects of Sedimentology, including the supplies of raw materials and fossil fuels that are so vital to the economy of the British Isles. The sedimentary environments discussed are related to examples of such environments from the geological past, thus illustrating how evidence for the movement of the region over geological time is preserved in rocks. In this way, many of the elements of Stratigraphy and Economic Geology present in Geology courses are covered.

The organisation of the material is such that different economic aspects are linked, chapter by chapter, into the appropriate parts of the text. For those wishing to concentrate on specific topics in Economic Geology, it is recommended that the relevant sub-sections be studied in the order given below.

Coal	Coal Swamps and Coal Measures	Book 2, p. 69
	Swamp Deposits to Coal	Book 1, p. 79
Coastal erosion	Coastal Defences	Book 2, p. 68
	Cliff Retreat	Book 1, p. 35
Heavy mineral deposits		
	Heavy Mineral Accumulations	Book 1, p. 35
	Diamond Prospecting	
	in Ancient Braided Streams	Book 2, p. 31
	Placer Gold in South Africa	Book 2, p. 32
Oil and gas	Oil Source Rocks	Book 2, p. 103
	The Formation of Oil and Gas	Book 1, p. 80
	Oil and Gas Reservoir Rocks	Book 1, p. 61
	Oil and Gas Reservoir Shapes	Book 1, p. 72
	Hydrocarbons in Deltas	Book 2, p. 71
	Hydrocarbons in Submarine Fans and	
	Turbidite Deposits	Book 2, p. 103
	Evaporite and Hydrocarbon Reservoirs	Book 2, p. 73

Practical work is an important element in science courses, and AS-level Geology syllabuses contain a significant practical element. Practical approaches should be an important part of A-level courses in Geology too, and in future syllabus changes the requirement for practical work is likely to be increased. Investigational practical work will probably also become a more significant part of degree courses in the future. Fieldwork is another essential element of all Geology and Earth Science courses, and the investigational aspects of fieldwork are also likely to be highlighted in future curriculum developments. It is with these factors in mind that the sections on *Practical Investigation and Fieldwork* have been devised. It is hoped that they will be of great value to student and teacher alike.

The sections entitled *Test Your Understanding* have been included, together with the questions in the figure captions, to encourage students to consider and evaluate the understanding they have gained from the text, and to apply it in new and different circumstances. This is precisely the approach used by professional and academic geologists during their exploration and research.

Geology and Earth Science have proved to be very rewarding areas of study for young people and adults alike, with many going on to careers in these fields or gaining hobbies for life. In both cases the approach used is that of the 'rock detective' as described in Chapter 1 in Book 1. Now that Earth Science has become an important element in school science syllabuses for 5- to 16-year-olds, we may expect that many more students will choose to study Earth Science in the future. One thing is certain: studies in Earth Science, including their sedimentological aspects, will continue to be vital to the economy of the British Isles, to the economy of the world, and to the conservation of the environment and resources of our planet, well into the twenty-first century and beyond.

Please note: all instances of the pronoun 'he' are to be interpreted as referring equally to both men and women.

INTRODUCTION

In *Sedimentology Book 1 – Processes and Analysis* we saw how scientists use the methods of the detective to study modern sediments and ancient sedimentary rocks so that the ancient rocks can be understood in terms of the processes active and the environments present at the surface of the Earth today. Part of this approach entails 'recreating the scene of the crime' by studying the different places on Earth where sediments are being deposited today. This means examining modern depositional environments.

When scientists study an environment in which sediments are being laid down today, what exactly do they study? The answers to this question may be found in *Sedimentology Book 1*, notably in Chapter 3, *What can the particles tell us? Analysing sediment*, and Chapter 4, *What can the sediment body tell us? Analysing the sediment body*. In Chapter 4 the sediment body is analysed by examining the following aspects:

A. the conditions of initiation;
B. the transportation and deposition of the sediments;
C. the sediment types;
D. the sedimentary structures;
E. the fauna and flora;
F. the geometry of the sediment body;
G. the resultant sequence.

This same framework will be used here, in *Sedimentology Book 2*, to examine depositional environments and the sediment bodies that are deposited there. Where possible, these sediment bodies will be illustrated by citing ancient, preserved examples of them, situated in various parts of the British Isles. The localities of these deposits and their positions in the geological column are summarised in Figure 0.1.

To help you understand the depositional environments to be studied in this book, we shall begin by looking at environments on land that you may already have visited, and so will know something about. We will then move on to less familiar environments, such as beneath the sea or in tropical or polar climates. This again is the approach of the detective, who works from what he knows towards what he does not know in order to gain a better understanding of 'the case in hand'.

Figure 0.1
The geological column, featuring the sedimentary sequences from different depositional environments preserved in Britain that are mentioned in the text. (The dates used are those of Snelling, 1985.)
What do these examples indicate:
(a) about the progressive changes in climate;
(b) about the change in sea depth/land height, in the area now Britain, since the Precambrian?
How might each of these changes be explained?

Geological period/system	Time (million years – m.y.)	Example of sedimentary sequence used in text	Location in Britain	Page
	0			
Quaternary		Fossil scree	Ecton Hill, Derbyshire	7
		Raised beaches	Scottish coast	45
		Glacial features	Lake District; Snowdonia; Scottish Highlands; Southern Uplands	28
		Braided meltwater streams	Thames Valley	14
	1.8			
Tertiary		Tidal flats and estuaries	south-east England	49
		Shallow sea sands and muds	south-east England	87
	65			
Cretaceous		'Chalk sea'	southern and eastern England	101
		Shallow sea sands } Quiet shallow sea muds }	eastern and southern England	86
	135			
Jurassic		Euxinic shelf conditions	Yorkshire to Dorset	86
		Quiet shallow seas	Yorkshire to Dorset	86
		Sabkha evaporites	Dorset	64
		Minor coal swamps	Yorkshire	71
		Delta/river conditions	Yorkshire	55
		Oolitic sand banks	Cotswolds; Bath area	62
		Euxinic shelf conditions	Yorkshire to Dorset	86
		Quiet shallow sea muds	Yorkshire to Dorset	86
	205			
Triassic		Saline giant evaporites	Cheshire Basin	67
		Braided streams	Cheshire Basin	14
		Desert dunes	Cheshire Basin	24
		Desert lakes	Cheshire Basin; Aust by the Severn Bridge	21
	250			
Permian		Saline giant evaporites	north-east England	67
		Desert dunes	Penrith, Cumbria; Devon; the Midlands	24
	290			
Carboniferous		Coal swamps	The coalfields of Britain	69
		Delta	The Peak District	54
		Submarine fan and turbidites	The Peak District	96
		Reefs and lagoons	The Peak District	61
	355			

continued on p. 3

Geological period/system	Time (million years – m.y.)	Example of sedimentary sequence used in text	Location in Britain	Page
	355			
Devonian		Semi-arid lake	Caithness, north-east Scotland	32
		Alluvial fan	Midland Valley of Scotland	8
		Meandering streams	South Wales	18
		Beach	North Devon	45
		Reefs and lagoons	South Devon	61
		Deep basins	North Cornwall	101
	405			
Silurian		Deep sea	Cumbria	100
		Tidal flats	Welsh Borderland; south-west Wales	49
		Shelf carbonates and patch reefs	Welsh Borderland	61
	435			
Ordovician		Shelf	South Wales and the Welsh Borderland	87
		Turbidites	West Wales	96
	510			
Cambrian		Deep sea	Southern Uplands	100
		Turbidites	North Wales	96
		Shelf	South Wales and the Welsh Borderland	87
	570			
Precambrian		Dalradian shelf sea	Jura and Islay in western Scotland	86
		Torridonian alluvial fans	north-west Scotland	8
		Torridonian braided streams	north-west Scotland	14
	4,600			

1. DEPOSITION ON THE CONTINENT

Depositional environments in continental areas (i.e. on land, in rivers, lakes, etc.) include those where deposition is caused mainly by gravity, such as scree areas, and those where water is the main agent, as on alluvial fans, in braided and meandering streams (**fluvial** i.e. river environments), lakes (**lacustrine** environments) and in some parts of desert and glacial areas. Also included are wind-dominated areas, as in deserts and some coastal and periglacial areas, and areas of ice erosion, transport and deposition in polar and mountain areas. All these environments, together with the sedimentary sequences that they are likely to produce, will be discussed in this chapter.

Scree and Alluvial Fan Environments

Screes and alluvial fans are the cone-shaped deposits that build up in or beside mountainous areas, as is shown in Figure 1.1. Screes are formed largely by gravity-controlled processes, as material falls from an exposed rock face to form a **scree** or **talus cone**. Similar underwater features are the talus deposits that form against reefs. Downslope, screes often develop into alluvial fan deposits. On fans, water is the main depositional agent, but it is only effective during storms. Normally the fairly steep alluvial fan surfaces are dry. Submarine fans are also known to develop where there is an abundant supply of sediment.

Conditions of initiation
The conditions of initiation that are required to trigger the formation of these types of deposit are the steep slopes and abundant supply of sediment found in rugged upland areas and, where there are relatively steep slopes, underwater.

Transportation and deposition of sediments
Transportation and deposition begins on the exposed rock face (the **free face**) where particles of rock have become loosened by weathering. They fall away from the free face under the influence of gravity, and slide, roll or bounce down, often aided in their movement by the presence of water. They come to rest at the foot of the free face where the slope changes and where any water currents spread out and slow down.

Sediment types
The sediment types involved are angular fragments of the parent rock and can have a variety of shapes and sizes. Such deposits are called **breccias**. The composition of the sediment grains – the **clasts** – depends entirely on the parent rock; the shapes of the clasts depend on the ways in which the rock has broken under the influence of weathering and erosion. The deposits are poorly sorted since there will have been little opportunity for the grains to become sorted out during transportation. The clasts remain angular for the same reason. Deposition occurs rapidly during storms and this, together with the angularity of the grains, produces a highly porous and permeable

Figure 1.1
Scree and fan deposits.
Why are underwater cone features less steep than those on the land surface?

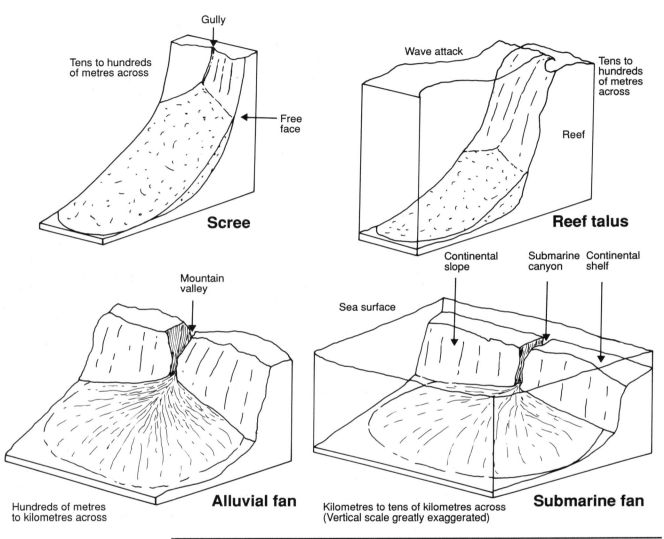

deposit. In fact, since water can pass freely between the grains, any fine-grained silts and clays can become washed out, thereby improving the sorting. However, it is also possible for fine materials to become washed in later, thus reducing the porosity and permeability of the deposit.

Sedimentary structures

Sedimentary structures are generally absent from screes, apart from a coarse layering or bedding that may sometimes be visible in cross-sections of fossil screes. The sedimentary structures found in fan deposits are very similar to those found in braided streams since fans usually change to braided stream deposits downslope. (The structures found in braided stream deposits are described on page 8.) In contrast, submarine fans tend to change to turbidity current deposits downslope and thus these deposits both have similar structures.

Fauna and flora

The fauna and flora of scree and fan deposits are very limited because these high-energy mobile environments are very difficult places for life to exist. Also, the preservation potential there for any fossil is extremely low – fossils form very rarely in coarse, highly porous, mobile deposits. The exception to this is the scree material formed beneath a reef. A reef is formed of dead and living organisms and so the talus material is actually a fossil deposit, i.e. it is composed of once-living material smashed from the reef by pounding waves.

Geometry of the sediment body

Screes and fans have the geometry of cut-away cones. This means that in cross-sectional view they are wedge shaped, and in plan view they are fan shaped, as shown in Figure 1.1. Neighbouring screes and fans frequently coalesce, i.e. join together, at their margins.

Resultant sequence

Resultant sequences of preserved screes and fans may show changes in sediment size up the sequence, as shown in Figure 1.2. You may be able to discover this for yourself by carrying out the fieldwork on a scree deposit suggested at the end of this chapter (see Investigation 2, page 34). However, as there are a variety of factors involved in scree formation, these deposits produce no typical resultant sequence. In geological terms, screes and fans are not commonly preserved since they form in steep environments which are usually subjected to later erosion. On **unconformity surfaces** (ancient erosion surfaces) **basal conglomerates** are often found (so called because they are coarse sediment deposits found at the base of the sequence overlying the unconformity). These basal conglomerates are fairly common and may have features typical of screes and fans.

Figure 1.2
Scree slope sequences.
Screes tend to coarsen downslope. As the scree builds out and up therefore, fining-upward sequences may develop near the base of the scree, whilst at the back of the scree, a sequence which fines, then coarsens upwards may develop. Why do screes tend to coarsen downslope?

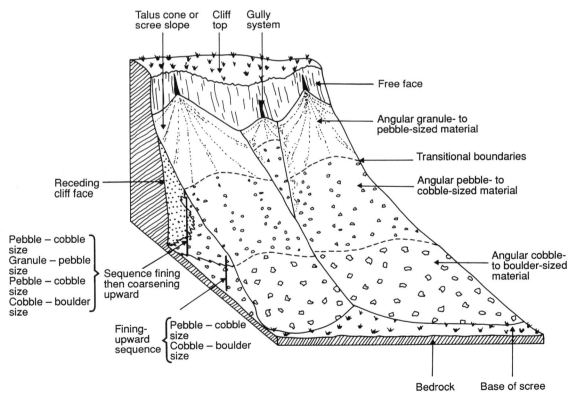

Examples in the British Isles

A good example of a fossil scree deposit may be found at Ecton Hill in Derbyshire. The scree was formed during the Pleistocene from a Carboniferous limestone parent rock. The angular fragments of the breccia have now become cemented by a carbonate cement, and red soil particles have become washed into the pore spaces between the particles.

Examples of alluvial fan deposits have been recognised in the Precambrian Torridonian sequences in north-west Scotland. Devonian alluvial fan deposits were well developed in the rift valley, active during Devonian times, which is now the Midland Valley of Scotland. In this valley, bounded by the Highland Boundary Fault to the north and the Southern Uplands Fault to the south, the fans were formed at the feet of the fault scarps by debris brought down from the upland areas on either side.

River (Fluvial) Environments

Two major types of river or fluvial environment are recognised: those dominated by braided stream conditions, and those where meandering processes are dominant.

Braided Streams

Conditions of initiation

Braided channels form wherever water runs over loose sand, so braided channel complexes can frequently be seen on beaches and quarry floors, and can also be produced on stream tables in the laboratory. Braided channels are so called because they look like braided or plaited hair. In fact the channels do not actually intertwine but they do split and rejoin frequently along curving paths. This is because the braiding process involves channel switching: as the water flows down the channel, it deposits sediment so that the channel eventually becomes too shallow to carry the water; the water then flows over the edge of the channel to form a new channel at the side. Thus the conditions of initiation necessary to form braided channels are flows of water carrying plenty of sediment. These conditions arise more frequently in higher-land, steeper-slope areas than in flat lowlands. Meandering channel conditions are more typical of flatter lowland areas.

Transportation and deposition of sediments

Braided streams can be found in most land environments on Earth. They are common in **periglacial** (ice-margin) areas, in desert regions and in upland areas of most countries, including Britain. Braided stream flows are flashy, i.e. they are irregular flows subjected to flash flooding from time to time. At times of high flow, large quantities of sediment are transported and later deposited. Transportation of the bedload is by **traction**, i.e. rolling and sliding, and by **saltation** or bouncing. Material is also carried in **suspension** and this is very obvious when streams are in flood, as the water is coloured by the sediment. Much dissolved material can also be carried in **solution**. The modes of transportation and deposition of the bedload and the sedimentary structures produced depend upon the size of the sediment and the velocity of water flow. The relationship between these variables has been investigated by experimentation in the laboratory, and the results are shown in Figure 1.3.

These results show that if a current of water is passed over a flat bed of medium grain-sized sand, at slow flows nothing initially happens to the sand. As the flow velocity is steadily increased, the sand grains become entrained and form **asymmetrical ripples** or **current ripples** as they move along. The grains are moved up the shallow slope of the ripple and deposited as a more steeply sloping lamination on the downstream side. In this way the ripples migrate downstream forming a rippled upper surface to the sand. The ripples show **cross-lamination** when seen in cross-section.

As the power of the current is steadily increased, a stage is reached when the ripples break down and larger **bedforms** called dunes, form instead. Such dunes formed underwater are called **subaqueous dunes**, to distinguish them from the wind-formed dunes found in deserts, on coasts, etc. Subaqueous dunes are very similar in shape to ripples but are larger, usually being between 0.5 and 10 metres across. They form in a similar way, in that sand grains are moved up the shallow, upstream side of the dune and accumulate at the top of the steep face. After a time this face becomes too steep and

Figure 1.3
Plot based on experimental work in the laboratory showing how sedimentary structures in sands evolve with increasing stream power. (Based on Allen, 1970.)
How could a sequence of plane bedding overlain by cross-bedded sands with cross-laminated sands above develop?

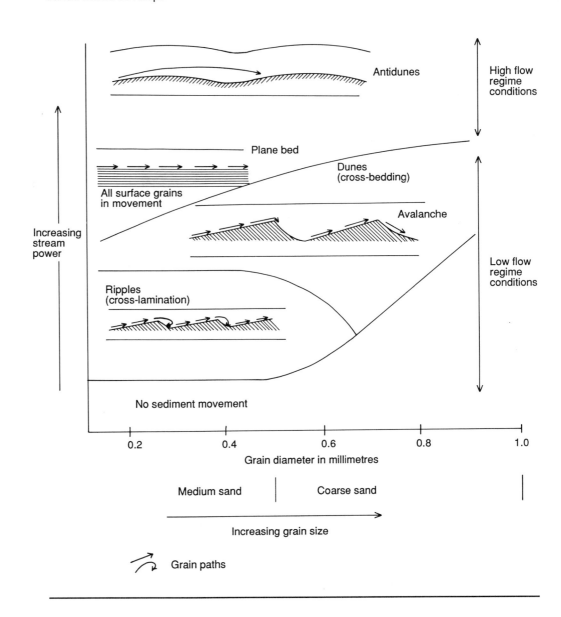

collapses in a small avalanche forming a sloping layer on the face. The sloping layers build up forming **cross-bedding** as the dune migrates downstream. If the dunes are straight they form **planar cross-bedding**; if curved, the beds of sand are deposited in the spoon-shaped hollows produced, thus forming **trough cross-bedding**, as shown in Figure 1.4.

During the formation of current ripples and dunes, not all the sand grains on the bed are in motion. In such circumstances **lower flow regime** conditions exist, as distinct from the **higher flow regime** conditions that occur at greater flow velocities. Under the higher flow conditions, all the grains on the surface of the sand bed are in motion. The dunes break down to form a flat bed or **plane bed** (not to be confused with planar cross-bedding). Plane bedding is thus characteristic of fast flows in high flow regime conditions. The surfaces of preserved plane beds may show a lineation in the direction of flow. This is called **primary current lineation**.

Figure 1.4
Varieties of cross-bedding: A – planar cross bedding produced by straight crested dunes; B – trough cross-bedding produced by lunate dunes. (Based on Allen, 1970.)
When palaeocurrent studies are carried out on trough cross-bedding, a large number of measurements has to be made. Why?

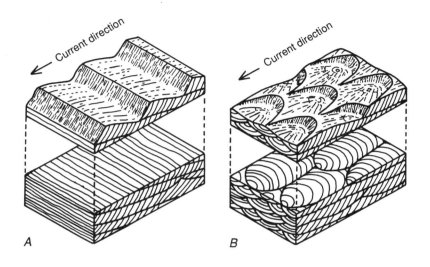

If the current velocity is increased still further, the plane bed breaks down to form a rolling sand surface of **antidunes**. At this stage the water is flowing so fast that it has waves on its upper surface. These are called **standing waves** since they do not move downstream. The standing waves may break to form white water. Antidunes differ from the dunes formed at lower flows in that the sand particles which are carried up the upstream slope of the antidune are not deposited at the top but are carried over to the upstream slope of the next dune, as shown in Figure 1.3 (see page 9). Thus, depending upon the balance between erosion and deposition, the antidunes may migrate upstream, or downstream, or may remain in the same position.

Antidunes are not commonly preserved in rivers because, as fast flowing currents slow down, they pass back through the sequence of events described and the high flow regime bedforms are destroyed. Plane beds are preserved more frequently since they are often buried by more layers of sand before the current slows.

This is the sequence of events for medium grain-sized sand but, as Figure 1.3 shows, ripples cannot form in coarse sands and so dunes are the first bedform to develop as the flow increases. Figure 1.3 also shows that the coarser the grain size of the sediment, the higher the flow velocity necessary to produce new sedimentary structures.

Sediment types

Having considered the modes of transportation and deposition in braided stream environments, we already know something of the types of sediment likely to be present there. The main types are gravels and sands, although silts are sometimes preserved in abandoned channels. Since braided streams tend to occur near sediment source areas, transportation distances are usually short, with the result that the sediments are immature (i.e. contain some of the less stable minerals), fairly angular and fairly poorly sorted. Since these sediments are frequently dumped by a waning flood, individual particles do not have time to adopt their most stable positions, so packing is generally poor, and this results in high porosity and permeability. Braided stream sediments may thus become well cemented and hard (**indurated**) during diagenesis as cement is deposited in the pore spaces.

Sedimentary structures

Of the different sedimentary structures produced during laboratory experimentation (see Figure 1.3), which are likely to be preserved in the braided stream environment? Antidunes are rare, as we might expect, since those that form are destroyed as flows decrease in power. However, plane bedding and cross-bedding are common, and massive or structureless beds are also frequently seen. Asymmetrical ripples are not very common because those that form during decreasing flows are frequently destroyed during the next flood. Asymmetrical ripple preservation is most likely during increasing flows when the structures are buried as they are formed.

Sometimes in braided streams a channel is abandoned and so the upper part of the channel becomes filled with finer-grained sediment such as fine sand and silt. In these circumstances ripples are likely to be preserved and the silt surface may dry out to produce **desiccation cracks** or mud cracks. Desiccation cracks form because, as the sediment dries out, the loss of water causes the sediment to shrink in all directions producing a polygonal pattern of V-shaped cracks on the surface, as shown in Figure 1.5. These may be preserved, particularly if the cracks become filled with sand in the next flood. If the abandoned channel silts are left for long enough, they may become colonised by vegetation. The roots of the vegetation may then become preserved as **rootlet beds** in the sequence. It should be stressed, however, that braided stream abandoned channel sequences are rare in comparison with the abandoned channels found in meandering stream sequences. As will be seen, meandering streams naturally produce abandoned channels whereas they are exceptional in braided streams.

Figure 1.5
Polygonal desiccation cracks caused by shrinkage during the drying out of mud.
These are preserved by a later sand infilling. Frequently colour differences are seen between the mud and the sand. Sometimes the sand infillings become concertinaed into folds. How?

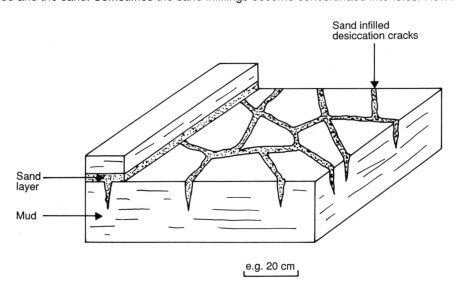

Fauna and flora

Fauna and flora are rarely preserved in braided stream environments for the same reasons as for scree and fan deposits, namely that little can live in the high energy environments, and preservation potential is low in fairly coarse, permeable, active sediments. Only in the rare abandoned channel sequences are plant fossils and fossils of small invertebrates, together with their tracks, trails and burrows, at all likely to be preserved.

Geometry of the sediment body

The geometry, particularly in plan view, is variable for braided streams. They can be confined to narrow valleys in upland areas, and downstream of valley glaciers, but preservation of these deposits in environments which are largely erosional is unlikely. However, where mountain streams and rivers pour out on to the plains below or where ice sheets melt in lowland areas, broad sweeps of braided streams can form and here preservation is likely, since these are depositional areas so that thick sequences can be built up. Preserved braided stream sequences are thus likely to be broad, fairly thick sheets, sometimes deposited on top of an erosional or unconformity surface.

Resultant sequence

Try to work out for yourself the resultant sequence likely to be produced in a braided stream environment such as the one shown in Figure 1.6. Draw a likely **stratigraphic log** for the sequence using the method shown in Figure 1.7 and the symbols given in Figure 1.8. The lowest part of a log has been drawn for you on Figure 1.6 to show how it could begin. A possible answer is given as part of Question 3 on page 36 (see Figure 1.28). Your attempt may not show as much variability as this answer but if you have got the general idea, you have done well.

Figure 1.6
A braided stream sequence. (From King, 1984.)
Make a copy of the graphic log outline started for you, below right. On it complete a likely typical log for the braided stream sequence, based on the right-hand corner of the block diagram. Use the method indicated in Figure 1.7 and the symbols given in Figure 1.8.

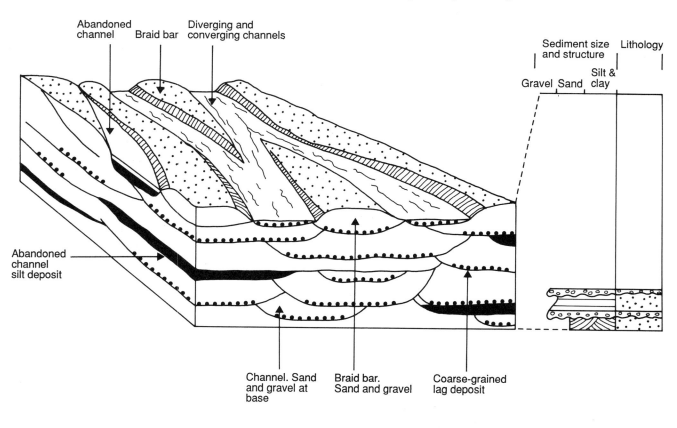

Figure 1.7
Method for drawing graphic logs.
The observations from the rock sequence are used as follows:
1. plot the bed bases in the correct positions in the lithology column;
2. shade in the correct lithologies (sediment types) in that column;
3. plot the graph of grain size on the left-hand side of the log;
4. add the structures (shown here as partially complete).
Why are these types of graphic log useful summaries of stratigraphic sequences?

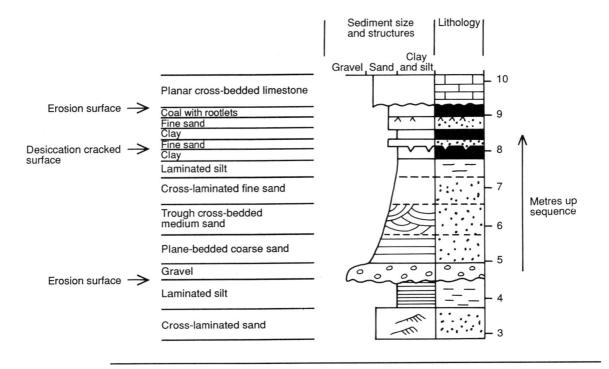

Figure 1.8
The symbols used for plotting graphic logs. (From Selley, 1970.)
Intraformational conglomerates contain lumps of mud eroded locally (i.e. from within the area of the rock formation) and deposited by the current. Extraformational conglomerates contain pebbles. Where do these pebbles come from?

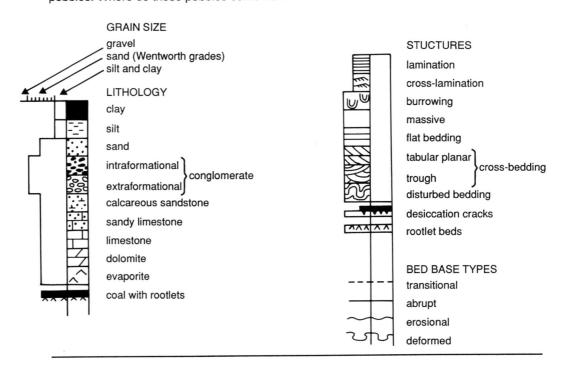

Examples in the British Isles

Preserved braided stream deposits are found in a number of areas of Britain. Good examples are the Precambrian Torridonian deposits of north-west Scotland and some of the Triassic sediments of the Cheshire Basin. More recent examples are the sweeps of sand and gravel deposited by melting ice sheets during the Pleistocene. The gravels of the Thames valley terraces were laid down by tumultuous floods caused in this way.

Meandering Streams

Conditions of initiation

Meandering streams develop when flows are fairly consistent and the stream is not overloaded with sediment. These conditions are found in relatively flat upland or lowland areas. Most streams and rivers that flow across plains meander.

Transportation and deposition of sediments

The transportation and deposition typical of meandering streams develop because fluids do not naturally flow in straight lines. Instead a corkscrew motion called a **helical flow** (flow like a helix) forms. This can be seen by stirring a cup of black tea. As the fluid circulates, floating tea leaves will be seen to move to the rim of the cup while the tea deposited in the bottom migrates to the centre. This is because the flow corkscrews around the cup, moving outwards at the surface and inwards at the base, as shown in cross-section in Figure 1.9.

Figure 1.9
Cross-section of a cup of black tea after stirring.
Tea leaves form a rotating deposit at the centre of the base of the cup while floating tea leaves are moved to the outside of the tea surface. This is because the stirring produces helical motion in the liquid, shown by the arrows. Where might floating particles accumulate on the bends of meandering streams?

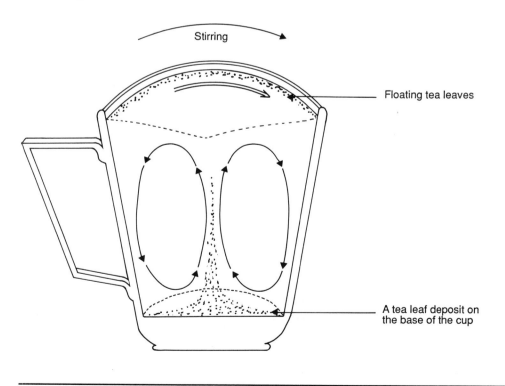

A river is a natural curving channel. At the outsides of bends, water is moving outwards and downwards. Aided by gravity this water flows fast and causes erosion. On the insides of bends, the water is flowing inward and upward against gravity. It therefore slows down causing the deposition of the sediment being carried. By erosion of the outside of the bend and deposition on the inside of the bend, the meander grows outwards, while staying the same width, as shown in Figure 1.10. Meanwhile, erosion also takes place on the downstream side of the meander bend so that, as the meander grows, it migrates downstream. The meander will eventually grow to a stable size but the downstream migration will continue (see Figure 1.11).

Figure 1.10
A meander channel in cross-section, showing channel migration by erosion of the outer part of the bend and deposition on the inner part of the bend.
Why do cut banks frequently collapse?

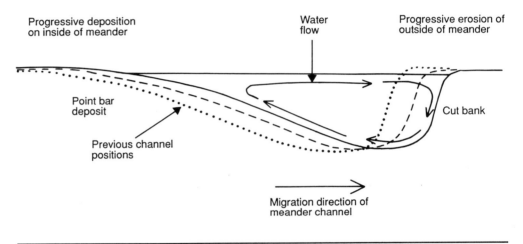

Figure 1.11
Downstream meander migration shown in plan view.
How might local farmers respond to meander migration? What remedial measures could they take?

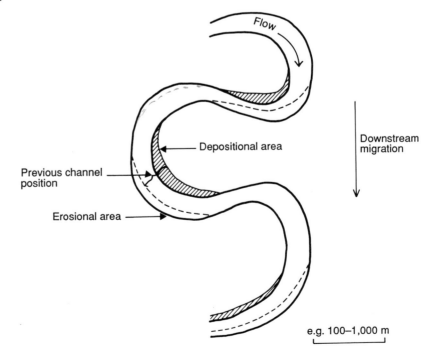

The meander channel environment is therefore a dynamic, i.e. moving, environment. On bends the outer eroded bank, the **cut bank**, is steep whereas the inner bank is a shallow depositional bank called the **slip-off slope**. The sediment found on the floor of the channel is gravel that is only moved during the high flow velocities of floods. This is called a **lag gravel** (it lagged behind while the finer sediment was moved on down the channel). Sand is deposited on the slip-off slope by the rising, slowing water current. As the current slows down, so finer sediment is deposited. Meander channel deposits tend therefore to be coarser at the base and to produce a fining-upward sequence, as is shown in Figure 1.12. The sands build up to form a curved bank, a **point bar**, on the inside of the meander bend. As the outer bank of the stream is eroded, so the point bar builds out over the lag gravel producing a channel sequence of gravel, covered by sloping sand beds whose sand becomes finer as it gets nearer the top. This is a fining-upward sequence that may be continued if fine-grained flood-plain silts and muds are later deposited on top.

Figure 1.12
The sedimentary sequence deposited by a laterally migrating meander channel seen in cross-section.
Why is planar cross-bedding more common than trough cross-bedding in point bar deposits?

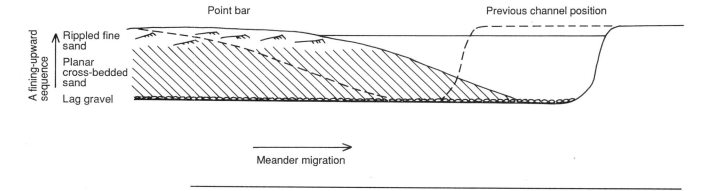

Migrating meanders sweep out a broad path for the meandering stream on the valley floor, eroding the valley sides whenever the outer bend of a meander comes against them. A broad valley floor which is cut by a series of meanders is called a **meander belt**. Where rock exposures form the valley sides, they may be steep free faces called **bluffs.**

A further complication that can arise as a result of meander migration is that necking may occur, as illustrated in Figure 1.13, causing a meander loop to be cut off. The abandoned channel, the **cut-off**, if full of water, forms a curved **ox-bow lake**. Mud deposits may settle out from the standing water in the abandoned channel. Sands or silts may be washed in during floods and the standing water replaced so that more mud can settle. Eventually the cut-off will become filled with sediment.

These are the main transportational and depositional activities that take place in the stream channel. A further very important part of the meandering stream environment is the flood plain, the relatively flat areas from the channel edges to the valley sides. These are the areas that are inundated during floods when the river 'bursts its banks'.

As sediment-laden water floods over the banks, the depth of the overflowing water is less than the water depth in the channel. Thus the increased friction on the water slows the flow down and causes sediment to be deposited. The first sediment to be deposited is sand. Then, as the water flows further away from the channel, it slows still further so that finer and finer grades of sediment are deposited. The sand is not carried far into the flood plain, and most of it is deposited on the channel banks. After several floods this can build up to form a higher natural bank, a **levée**, to the river. (This should not be confused with the banks often constructed on the banks of meandering rivers such

Figure 1.13
The necking process forming abandoned meander loops.
Why is necking more likely during floods?

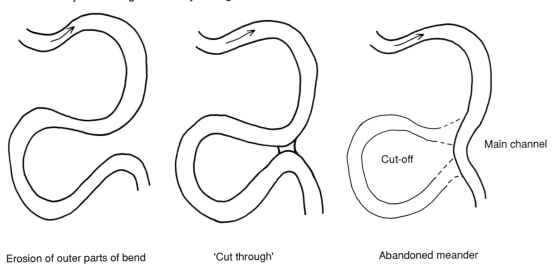

Erosion of outer parts of bend   'Cut through'   Abandoned meander

as the Mersey to stop them from flooding. Though also called levées, these have been built as flood defences.) It is during major floods that erosion on the outside of a meander causes a natural levée (or indeed a constructed levée) to be breached. The water flows fast through the gap – the **crevasse** – created, to form a sheet of water over the flood plain below. It is on the flood plain that the silts are deposited and eventually, as the flood waters subside, a layer of mud is laid down over the area. The mud hardens and cracks as the flood plain dries out.

Sediment types
The sediment types found therefore in meandering stream environments are sands, silts and muds, with thin layers of gravel on the floors of channels. Much of this sediment has travelled far and so is fairly mature and fairly well sorted with sub-angular to sub-rounded grains. Deposition is generally at slower rates than in braided stream environments and so packing tends to be better, resulting in lower porosities and permeabilities.

Sedimentary structures
As we have seen, there are three different depositional areas associated with meandering stream environments: the active channels, the abandoned channels, and the flood plain. Each of these areas has its characteristic sediments, sedimentary structures and fauna and flora, which enable it to be recognised in preserved sequences.

In active channels, lag gravels are deposited on the floor and these may be **imbricated** i.e. lie like roofing slates, each one partially overlapping the next. On top of the lag gravel, the fining-upward point bar sequence is laid down. Since the sands are deposited on a flat sloping surface they build up as planar cross-beds. Towards the finer top of the sequence, where currents are slower, asymmetrical ripples may be found. The complete sequence is shown in Figure 1.12 (see page 16).

Abandoned channels are likely also to be floored by imbricated lag gravels which were deposited before the channel was abandoned. However, once abandoned they are characterised by fine-grained sediment. The mud that settles from suspension is likely to be laminated and when floods wash in thin beds of sand, these may well contain asymmetrical ripples. The ox-bow lakes may dry out from time to time producing desiccation cracks in the mud.

The flood plain is the broadest depositional area associated with meandering streams, and the sediments tend to become finer the further away they are from the channels. On the banks levées form, with cross-bedded or rippled sands. These fine outwards into laminated silts and muds. This is the normal pattern. Where the levée was first breached during a flood, however, the water flowing through the crevasse deposits a fan-shaped **crevasse splay** sand deposit as a sheet over the area. As the flood plain sediments drain and dry out, features typical of this process can be formed, such as rills in the sands and desiccation cracks in the muds. Rain showers may leave rain pits and animals can leave tracks and trails. These are key features enabling geologists to identify environments that have dried out, i.e. continental and coastal environments.

Fauna and flora
In the active channel environment few fossils of any type are preserved. The abandoned channels, having a low energy, fine-grained environment, are not only good areas for pond organisms to live in, but they also have good preservation potential.

When they die, the pond organisms that live near the oxygenated surface fall to the bottom where, due to the poor circulation and the accumulated organic material, there is a lack of oxygen, i.e. **anaerobic** or **euxinic** conditions prevail. Most of the bacteria which cause organisms to decay cannot work in these anaerobic conditions. This explains the very good preservation potential of both plant and animal fossils in the abandoned channel muds.

Flood plain environments are generally poor areas for invertebrates to live in, but on rare occasions, as flood plain pools evaporate, large numbers of fish can become trapped and eventually preserved as fossils. If the flood plain does not flood too frequently then vegetation can colonise the area, producing rootlet beds and eventually soils that can be preserved. The calcretes found in the Devonian deposits of South Wales are considered to be preserved calcic soils that formed in a fairly arid flood-plain environment.

Geometry of the sediment body
The geometry of the sediment body deposited by a meandering stream or river is fairly broad and flat, relatively thin and very long. As a result these bodies are sometimes called **shoe string sands** because of their likeness to a long, flat shoe lace. Where neighbouring streams come together, broad sheets of meandering stream sediments can develop.

Resultant sequence
The normal resultant sequence for a meandering stream is a fining-upward channel sequence capped by a finer flood-plain deposit with scattered abandoned channels throughout the sediment body. In sedimentary rocks thought to have been laid down by meandering streams the fining-upward sequence is often seen to be repeated. This has been related to change in base levels, i.e. periodic subsidence of the land or, possibly, but much less likely, periodic changes in sea level. This cyclicity is preserved as a sequence of fining-upward cycles, as is shown in Figure 1.14. Using the same method as for the braided stream resultant sequence (see Figures 1.6–1.8, pages 12-13) draw a likely stratigraphic log for a meandering stream sequence, based on the right-hand corner of the block diagram in Figure 1.14. A possible answer is given as part of Question 3 at the end of this chapter (see Figure 1.28, page 36).

Examples in the British Isles
The best known example in Britain of meandering stream cycles with their associated sediments, sedimentary structures and calcretes is the Devonian deposits of South Wales mentioned above.

Figure 1.14
A meandering stream sequence.
Make a copy of the graphic log outline shown below right. On it, draw a likely typical log for a meandering stream sequence, based on the right-hand corner of the block diagram. Use the method of Figure 1.7 and the symbols of Figure 1.8 (page 13).

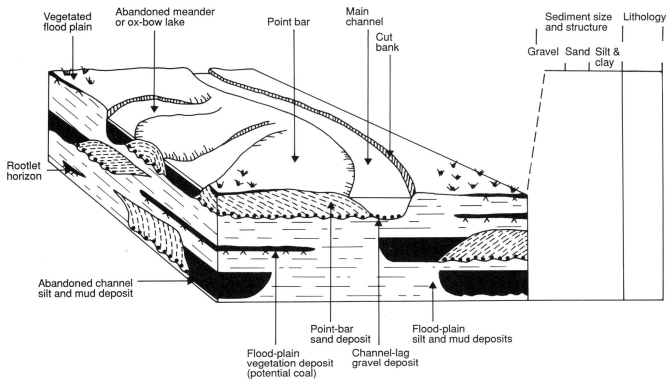

Desert Environments

Deserts are regions of the Earth where potential evaporation exceeds rainfall, so standing water is rarely found in these arid and semi-arid areas. Although the features of hot and cold deserts are similar, the arid areas near the great ice sheets are best considered with glacial sedimentation. Deposition in hot deserts will be our main concern in this section.

Several different types of modern desert surface are recognised and three of the major ones are known by their Arabian names. The **hammada** or bare rock surfaces are the main source of sediment for the other areas and have often been sand blasted into strange sculptured rock formations. The **regs** are the stony deserts formed when mixed sediment deposited by infrequent desert floods has had the fine-grained silt **winnowed away** by the wind (winnowing was the technique used by corn threshers in the past, using the wind to separate the light chaff from the heavier corn grains). This causes a **deflation** or lowering of the surface as the coarser particles which cannot be moved by the wind become concentrated. Some of the pebbles on the desert floor also become sand blasted, such that a smooth surface is eroded on the upwind side. If these pebbles become flipped over in a subsequent flood, more than one surface can become smoothed, producing a triangular shape with sharp corners. This process is shown in Figure 1.15. Such sculptured pebbles can only form under these conditions and so are good indicators of wind-dominated environments. They are known either by the French-derived name of **ventifacts** (wind-formed artifacts) or by the German-derived term **dreikanters** (referring to their three sides).

Figure 1.15
The formation of ventifacts by wind-driven sand and the effect of rolling by flood water.
How might the pebbles originally have been deposited on the desert floor?

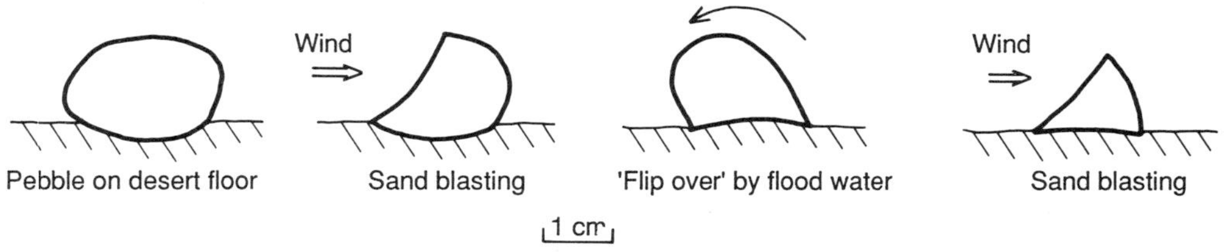

Wind ⇒

Pebble on desert floor   Sand blasting   'Flip over' by flood water   Wind ⇒   Sand blasting

⌐1 cm⌐

Hammada and regs together make up about 50–60 per cent of deserts and as these areas are largely erosional, they are of interest to geologists only in as much as they are the source of desert sediment. Large desert areas dominated by sand dunes are called sand seas, and are known by the Arabian name of **erg**. These are important depositional environments but they are not as widespread in desert regions as many people imagine. Other important depositional areas in desert environments are alluvial fans and ephemeral streams, desert lakes and coastal lowland areas.

Ephemeral Streams and Alluvial Fans

Ephemeral means short-lived, and in this case it pertains to the streams that form during torrential desert storms. The floods formed by these storms often move and redeposit much sediment before fading away as the water infiltrates into the ground or evaporates. These are braided streams. Braided stream environments, as well as alluvial fans, have been considered already (see pages 5 and 8), so will not be discussed further here.

Desert Lakes

The streams that form during storms can flood many lowland areas forming widespread shallow desert lakes called **playas**. Playas contain typical fine-grained, laminated **lacustrine** (lake) sediments, but being desert sediments they are rich in iron. As the waters of the ephemeral playas evaporate, evaporite minerals such as halite often crystallise out and may become preserved in the lake sediments. The soluble halite can then be dissolved by water in the next flood, leaving moulds. If these moulds are later filled by lake floor silts, casts are formed which are **pseudomorphs** of the original halite crystals. When the silts become siltstones and the underlying layers are eroded, the pseudomorphs are found on the bases of the silt beds. Sometimes well-developed halite crystals with stepped faces, called **hopper crystals**, are pseudomorphed in this way, as shown in Figure 1.16.

Figure 1.16
The formation of salt pseudomorphs.
How might salt pseudomorphs be used to find out if siltstones have been turned upside-down by folding?

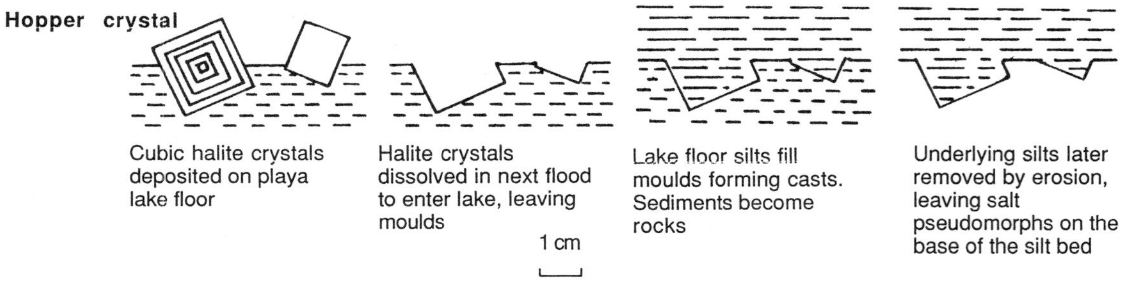

Hopper crystal

Cubic halite crystals deposited on playa lake floor   Halite crystals dissolved in next flood to enter lake, leaving moulds   Lake floor silts fill moulds forming casts. Sediments become rocks   Underlying silts later removed by erosion, leaving salt pseudomorphs on the base of the silt bed

1 cm

Playa lake sediments containing typical features such as wave ripples, desiccation cracks and halite pseudomorphs are to be found in the Triassic rocks of the Cheshire Basin and of Aust Cliff on the banks of the Severn Estuary near Bristol. Some of these silts, which were deposited in desert lakes, became cemented by the crystallisation of calcium carbonate in the pore spaces as the salt desert water evaporated. These Triassic carbonate-cemented siltstones are called **marls**.

The sediments and evaporites deposited in desert coastal lowlands will be dealt with in Chapter 2.

Dunes

Most sediments in deserts are initially deposited by water but they may be later **reworked** by the wind. Wind, like water, is a fluid, and the processes of erosion, transportation and deposition caused by wind are very similar to those caused by water. This has been demonstrated by experiments which have led to graphs being drawn for wind, like the Hjulstrom graph for water (see page 32 in *Sedimentology Book 1*). These graphs show entrainment and depositional velocities etc. for different grades of sediment. The main difference between water and wind to emerge from these experiments is that wind is unable to move the coarser grades of sediment. Wind transports sediment in the same way that water does, i.e. bedload is transported by rolling, sliding and saltation, and finer grade material is carried in suspension. The fine-grade desert sediments are usually carried out of the area, then deposited on desert margins as desert dust – **loess** – deposits, or else they are carried out over the oceans before falling from suspension in the air into the water and eventually settling to the ocean bed. The mobile sediments that remain in the deserts are the sands and it is these that are available to form dunes.

Three different scales of dune-like bedforms have been recognised in deserts. The smallest are asymmetrical wind ripples which are centimetres across and which form in the same way as current ripples in water. **Aeolian dunes**, formed like subaqueous dunes, are tens to hundreds of metres across and can be tens of metres high. **Draas** are the largest of these bedforms, being hundreds of metres to kilometres across and often hundreds of metres high. They are so large, in fact, that they are difficult to perceive on the ground and are best seen on satellite photographs. Usually, draas carry dunes on their backs and dunes, in turn, carry asymmetrical ripples.

Conditions of initiation

The first condition of initiation necessary for the formation of dunes by wind is the presence of winds of suitable velocities. These winds require wide open spaces with no obstacles such as vegetation which would reduce their speed. The second condition of initiation is the presence of loose (i.e. unconsolidated) sediment of the right grain size. The right grain size is one that is not so coarse that the particles cannot be moved by wind, and not so fine that the sediment is blown out of the area in suspension. These conditions occur in three very different environments, as described below.

The first such environment is coasts where onshore winds reach high velocities having blown over wide ocean areas, and where the loose beach sediments are the source of the sand for these coastal dunes. There are many coastal dune fields along the coasts of the British Isles and you can investigate one for yourself by following the guide in the *Practical Investigation and Fieldwork* section of this chapter (see page 35).

A second area of dune formation is in periglacial areas. Cold dense air frequently sweeps down from the large ice sheets and can form dunes from the sand-grade material of recently deposited glacial sediments. These winds also blow the silt-grade material out of the area, depositing widespread loess deposits beyond the periglacial regions. The thick and extensive loess deposits laid down over vast areas of central Europe, eastern South America and China were formed in this way.

The third area of dune formation is of course the deserts, where various types of dune form under different circumstances. Four main desert dune types can be recognised: transverse dunes, barchans, stellate dunes and longitudinal dunes.

Transportation and deposition of sediments

Transverse dunes form at right angles to the path of the prevailing wind (i.e. transverse to it). They have straight or slightly sinuous crests, a shallow windward slope and a steep lee slope, as is shown in Figure 1.17. The formation process of aeolian transverse dunes is very similar to that of subaqueous dunes, i.e. the sand is moved up the windward slope by rolling, sliding and saltation (bouncing), often forming asymmetrical

Figure 1.17
Transverse dunes.
How do these aeolian dunes compare with the straight crested subaqueous dunes that produce planar cross-bedding?

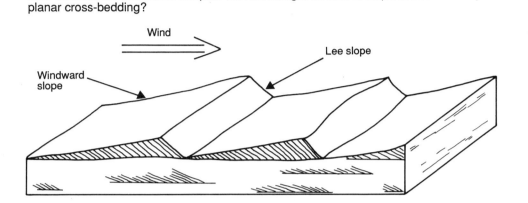

ripples as it is moved. It accumulates at the crest of the dune, building out the upper part of the steep lee slope. Eventually this steepening slope reaches its **angle of yield**, i.e. becomes unstable, and collapses in an avalanche to form a layer of sand over the lee face at a more shallow angle, the **angle of rest** of the loose sand. As erosion of the windward side of the dune continues and more and more sloping sand beds are deposited on the lee side, the transverse dune migrates downwind, forming a large-scale cross-bedded sequence as it does so, the cross-beds dipping in the wind direction. Large-scale cross-beds (cross-bed sets often more than a metre in height) with typical curved surfaces are only rarely formed in other circumstances and so are good indicators of wind deposition in fossil sand dunes.

Barchans are the famous crescent-shaped sand dunes (see Figure 1.18). Like transverse dunes, these have a shallow windward slope and a steep lee slope and they form in a very similar way. The difference is that barchans are isolated dunes which tend to migrate across hard desert surfaces, such as old lake beds. They are high in the centre

Figure 1.18
Barchan dunes.
How does the crescent shape of these aeolian dunes develop?

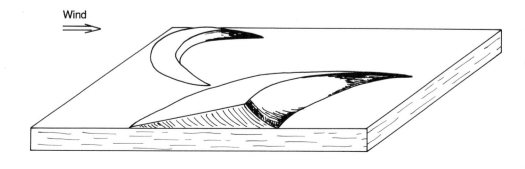

and peter out towards the margins. As there is less sand in the dune margins, they can be moved faster by the wind than the bulk of the dune and so develop into 'horns' pointing down-wind. This is the way in which the curved barchan shape develops.

Stellate dunes or **rhourds** are 'star shaped', i.e. they have a high centre with a series of dune crests radiating away in various directions (see Figure 1.19). These dunes can be tens of metres high, and they do not migrate. They seem to form where there is no obvious prevailing wind direction.

Figure 1.19
A stellate dune.
What are the conditions of initiation necessary to form this type of dune?

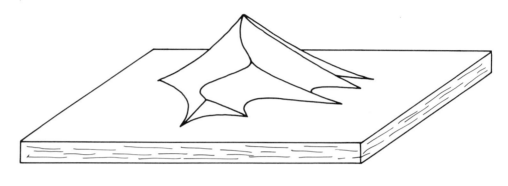

Seifs or **longitudinal dunes** form parallel to the wind direction and their formation process differs from that of the other desert dunes. As the wind blows down the corridor between the dunes, it develops two corkscrew vortices. This helical motion erodes sand from the floor of the inter-dune corridor and deposits it in dipping beds on the side of the dune, as is shown in Figure 1.20. As the sand is deposited in this fashion on both sides, a fairly symmetrical dune shape develops. The sediment remaining in the inter-

Figure 1.20
Seif dunes.
How is the internal structure of the dunes, as shown here, formed?

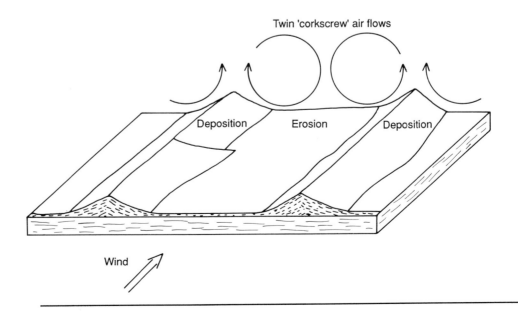

dune area is either too coarse to be moved by wind or is fine, hard desert lake sediment. A size frequency distribution for this sediment shows that it is poorly sorted and bimodal, with a gravel mode and a silt mode. Seifs cannot migrate, although the sediment may migrate along them. Dune fields like this are easy to cross by travelling along the dune corridors, but extremely difficult to cross at right angles to the dunes!

Sediment types
The sediment types involved in dune formation range from coarse silt to coarse sand. The sediments are usually very mature in deserts (less so in coastal and periglacial areas), having been transported by wind over long distances. This also produces very good sorting of the dune sands – in fact, the best sorting of any natural circumstances. Dune sand grains in deserts become well rounded by many collisions with other grains and often have pitted or frosted surfaces. They also frequently have a red, iron-rich desert varnish on the surface. As they are deposited fast by avalanching, packing is poor and this, together with the good sorting, causes dune sands to have high porosities and permeabilities.

Sedimentary structures
Large-scale cross-bedding is a key feature of dunes. Ripple cross-lamination is rare.

Fauna and flora
Signs of flora or fauna in desert or periglacial dune sands are unusual. Coastal dunes, however, may contain a fairly high percentage of shell material blown from the beach.

Geometry of the sediment body
The geometries of dunes have been shown in Figures 1.17, 1.18, 1.19 and 1.20. Cross-sections of all these dune types show high points in the centre with beds of sand dipping downward towards the dune margins.

Resultant sequence
Since barchans form in areas starved of sand and neither stellate dunes nor seifs migrate, there is no process by which these dunes can be preserved. Only transverse dunes are likely to become fossilised because they form where there is plenty of sand. This allows them to climb over and bury down-wind dunes, and if this occurs in a subsiding area, dune fossilisation is likely. This is particularly so if the dune sands sink beneath the water table because the damp sand is much more difficult to erode than dry sand. Any dunes colonised by vegetation will have become stabilised by the plants' powers of **baffling** (slowing down of the wind currents) and **binding** (by the roots), and so are unlikely to be preserved. Therefore only mobile transverse dunes are likely to produce a resultant sequence, and this will be of the type shown in Figure 1.21.

Examples in the British Isles
Fossilised sand dunes are found in the Permian rocks of Britain, particularly in Cumbria, near Penrith in north-west England, in parts of the Midlands and in Devon. Triassic dune sands are found in the Cheshire Basin area. Palaeocurrent studies of these dunes indicate that the prevailing palaeowinds were from the east and north-east, the

Figure 1.21
The resultant sequence that might form in areas dominated by transverse dunes.
Why is a rising water table likely to be an important control on wind erosion?

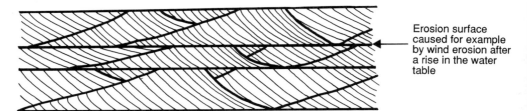

Erosion surface caused for example by wind erosion after a rise in the water table

same directions in which the trade winds blow over the Sahara desert today. This is good evidence that the latitude of Britain at that time was similar to the latitude of the Sahara today, i.e. near the Tropic of Cancer.

Glacial Environments

The agents of erosion, transportation and deposition on continents are gravity (as in screes), running water (alluvial fans, rivers and lakes), wind (desert, coastal and periglacial dunes) and ice. Ice processes require a mean temperature of less than 0° C, freezing point. This occurs today at high latitudes (the Arctic and Antarctic) and in mountainous areas. These are the areas, therefore, where we can study glacial processes in action.

During the ice ages of the Pleistocene, ice sheets developed much further from the poles than they are found today. At one time during this period Britain was covered by an ice sheet extending as far south as a line from the River Thames to the Severn Estuary and the north coast of Devon and Cornwall (called the Thames-Severn Line). South of this line **periglacial** i.e. ice margin, processes were active. Thus the present-day topography of the whole of Britain, as well as many other northern hemisphere countries, owes a great deal to these glacial episodes which were relatively recent in geological terms, ending only about 10,000 years ago.

It should be made clear, however, that between the glacial episodes of the Pleistocene, in the periods of time called **interglacials**, Britain was frequently much warmer than it is today. Indeed, sub-tropical faunas and floras have been preserved in the sediments laid down during the interglacial periods. Thus the Pleistocene was a time of greatly fluctuating temperatures which had dramatic effects upon the geology and the geography of Britain, and the world as a whole.

The trigger, i.e. conditions of initiation, of an ice age, or rather, of a series of ice ages, is unknown. Major world-wide ice ages are rare events in geological terms, only two being recognised in the Precambrian, one in the Ordovician, one during the Carboniferous and Permian and the most recent one in the Quaternary. At present about 10 per cent of the Earth's area is covered by ice, but during the Pleistocene it is estimated that up to 30 per cent of the Earth's surface was ice-covered, locking up an enormous quantity of water on the land and sea surfaces and resulting, therefore, in large-scale lowerings of sea level. Thus **eustatic** (i.e. world-wide) fluctuations in sea level occurred during the Pleistocene; sea level was low during the glacials and higher than now during the interglacials. This has produced important effects, particularly on our coastlines where **raised beaches** can be found. These are ancient beaches, often backed by cliffs, now found as near-horizontal surfaces tens of metres above present-day beaches. In other areas **drowned forests** can be seen, where trees were drowned by the rising sea and are now preserved as fossils below present-day sea level, only being exposed sometimes at low tide.

Britain has been affected in the past both by large ice sheets like those that cover Antarctica and Greenland today, and, on upland areas, by smaller scale mountain glaciation as is now found in Norway, British Columbia, etc. Although the processes involved in the formation of both these types of glacial environments are similar, the scale and distribution of the deposits formed are rather different, so it is best to separate them for our purposes. However, it should be remembered that mountain glaciation must precede the advance of continental ice sheets, and it will also remain as glacial remnants when the major ice sheets retreat.

The term retreat, used to describe the movement of an ice front towards the poles, or uphill in mountainous areas, can be misleading. It does not mean that the ice itself moves backwards during a retreat, but rather that the melting of the ice is faster than the ice sheet can move forward, thus producing a net backward movement of the ice face or **snout** of a glacier.

The Effects of Large Ice Sheets

Erosion

Continental ice sheets move like large-scale abrasives over the landscape, flattening out irregularities in their paths, and gouging out large areas of softer rocks, while big areas of resistant rocks remain, 'standing out' once the ice has gone. Huge floating tongues of ice move down any north–south extending sea areas. In Britain during the last glaciation the Irish Sea tongue of ice came on shore at Anglesey and eroded it almost flat. The Snowdonia massif, however, was composed of more resistant rock and therefore remained upstanding. Meanwhile, to the east, the soft rocks of the Cheshire Basin were hollowed out to give the Cheshire lowlands of today. Similar effects can be seen in other regions of the country, north of the Thames–Severn Line.

The erosion caused by these ice sheets is largely covered by glacial deposits. These are of two types: those deposited directly by melting ice, called **meltout deposits**, and those deposited or reworked by the glacial meltwaters.

Meltout deposits

The meltout deposits are the unsorted materials of glacial erosion, i.e. boulders, sands and clay grade material. These deposits are called **till**. Till is recognised by its unsorted nature and the fact that the boulders etc. (the clasts) are randomly orientated in and scattered through the clay. The clasts are usually angular and some of them are scratched or striated. Till can be deposited under differing circumstances forming different forms of **moraine**. The two major types of moraine deposited by continental ice sheets are **terminal moraine** and **ground moraine**. Terminal moraine is simply the material dumped at the end or terminus of the ice sheet as an untidy hummocky ridge along the face of the ice. More than one terminal moraine can form as an ice sheet melts and retreats, because a ridge of till develops wherever the ice front remains in the same position for some time.

Ground moraine is the hummocky blanket of till deposited by the ice over large areas of lowland. It is either smeared on to the ground surface at the base of the ice sheet as the sheet moves forward, or is deposited as the ice sheet melts and retreats. It can be recognised by the characteristics described below. As it is largely composed of very fine-grained material, the ground moraine is usually impermeable, producing heavy, poorly-drained clay soils. Any depressions fill with water forming small lakes and ponds. During the retreat of the ice, some large lumps of stagnant ice may be left behind. If till accumulates around these, when the ice melts it will leave large holes in the till blanket, called **kettle holes**, and these frequently become filled with water too. Sometimes ground moraine, or other deposits from the base of the ice, become shaped into 'swarms' of hummocks shaped like whale backs and called **drumlins**. The drumlins are often arranged *en echelon*, i.e. arranged like a flight of geese or a formation of ships. The mode of formation of drumlins is not well understood, but they are useful because they have shallow slopes facing down-ice (as shown in Figure 1.22) and so preserved drumlins indicate the direction of movement of the ice sheet.

Ice-movement directions can also be shown by **erratics** found in glacial till. These are boulders, pebbles, etc. of **exotic rocks**, i.e. rocks that do not outcrop in the area where they have been found. The erratics must therefore have been transported into the area by the ice and, on occasion, will have been carried for very long distances. If the rock is easily identifiable and the area where the source rock is exposed is known, then the direction of the ice movement can be plotted. A very good example of this is the unique Ailsa Craig granite which forms a small island to the south of Arran in Scotland. Erratics of this granite have been found in various places down the east coast of Ireland, in Cumbria, Lancashire, North Wales and Pembrokeshire in South Wales. These finds show that the Irish Sea ice sheet that eroded Ailsa Craig carried its debris south, as far as South Wales at least, before depositing it. They also show that the ice sheet came onshore at many places on the margin of the Irish Sea.

Another example of the value of erratics in plotting the directions of ice movement is the finds of Cumbrian Shap granite clasts in the Lancashire and Cheshire lowlands and

Figure 1.22
A summary diagram of the deposits of ice sheets, both by meltout and by meltwater.
Which deposits are which? How could you distinguish them in the field?

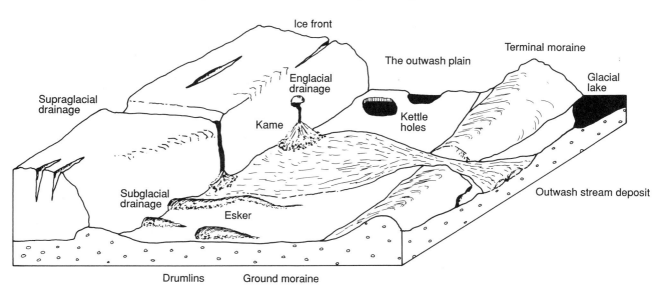

on the beaches of north-east England. These finds show that ice flowed away from the Lake District both towards the south and across the Pennines towards the east coast.

Erratics of rhomb porphyries, an igneous rock of Scandinavian origin, can be found in the beach gravels of north-east England as well, showing that the North Sea ice sheet was able to transport material right across the North Sea area before dumping it on the east coast of Britain.

Meltwater deposits

Meltwater can run *over* the surface of an ice sheet (**supraglacial drainage**), *within* an ice sheet in caves (**englacial drainage**), and also *at the base* of a sheet (**subglacial drainage**). This water flows out of the ice front and away across the **outwash plain** beyond the ice margin (see Figure 1.22, above). Most glacial meltwater reworking and deposition takes place on the outwash plain, but the other meltwater streams also produce some characteristic deposits.

During large-scale melting, water floods across outwash plain areas as braided streams, sorting and redepositing the gravels and sands and carrying much of the silt- and mud-grade material away. In the depressions left in the landscape, glacial lakes form and some of the fine-grained sediments are deposited by settling in the relatively still lake waters. Such glacial lakes build up strongly layered deposits called **varves**, as shown in Figure 1.23. Varves form because during warm periods, much meltwater and sediment comes into the lake. The pale-coloured silts settle out forming a fairly thick layer. However, as colder times approach, less and less meltwater and sediment reach the lake and eventually it freezes over. In the quiet frozen conditions, with no sediment supply, the fine-grained darker muds settle out forming a thinner dark layer. Pale layers grade gradually upwards into the darker layers because of the gradual freezing. Warming often occurs suddenly in glacial areas, producing sudden melting and an abrupt change from a dark layer to a paler layer. This cycle of warming and cooling often reflects an annual change, in which case one varve is produced each year. However, temperatures may fluctuate during the year, leading to more than one varve being produced in that year. Exceptional years can be seen because excessive melting will produce thicker than usual pale layers, while cold years will have relatively thin pale layers.

Figure 1.23
Glacial varves – rhythmic layers formed in glacial lakes by seasonal changes.
How many years does this diagram represent assuming that each varve represents one year?
Why are thick dark layers likely to follow thick pale layers?

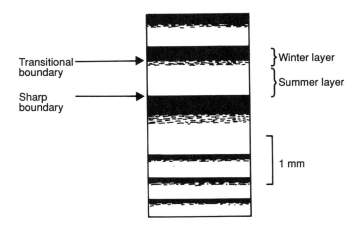

Varves are very useful to geologists for two reasons. First, since they can only form under ice-margin conditions, when they are found they are good indicators of past glacial environments. Second, sequences of varves from different areas have been recognised and then correlated with one another. As a result it has been possible to work out accurate ages, in years, of preserved lake sediments from the not too distant past. For example, glacial lake sediments in Scandinavia 8,000 years old have been dated by this method.

Not all the fine-grained glacial sediment is deposited in varves. Much of the silt and clay is carried out of the immediate area by the meltwater streams and is then eventually carried to the sea, where it is deposited in coastal tidal flats or on the ocean floor.

The meltwater that flows *through or over* the ice sheet sorts the sediment. The meltwater carries the silt and clay beyond the ice sheets, while most of the sand and gravel are carried to the edge of the sheet and are dumped in heaps at the ice face. Such piles of meltwater sand and gravel dumped from time to time over the flood plain are called **kames**.

Meltwater that flows *at the base* of the ice sheet usually carves itself a winding channel or ice cave in which to flow. Sands and gravels are deposited on the floor of the cave, so that after the ice has gone a ridge of sand and gravel winding over the outwash plain remains. Such ridges are called **eskers** and they show, by their orientations, the general trend of meltwater and ice movement. Esker deposits that are wide in some places and narrower in others are called **beaded eskers**.

All the ice sheet deposits described above, both meltout and meltwater, are shown in the rather simplified summary diagram Figure 1.22 (see page 27).

The Effects of Mountain Glaciation
For obvious reasons, the effects of mountain glaciation are seen only in highland areas of Britain, such as the Scottish Highlands, Southern Uplands, Lake District and North Wales.

Erosion
Glaciation of upland areas leaves a number of characteristic landforms which are very good evidence for a previous glaciation. These include the **corries, arêtes, horns, U-shaped valleys** and **hanging valleys** shown in Figure 1.24. These are all formed by the abrasion of moving ice. They will not be discussed here in detail as we are more

Figure 1.24
A summary diagram of landforms produced by glacial erosion of upland areas.
How might landforms like these be orientated in a dome-shaped highland area such as the Lake District?

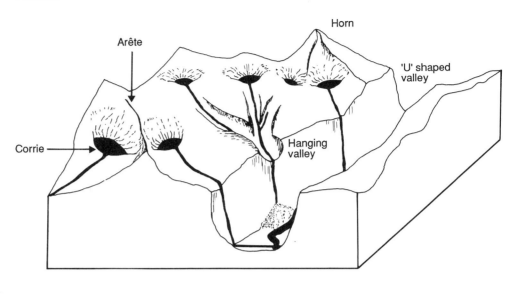

concerned with the deposits of the ice than with the effects of ice erosion. Erosive features that are useful, however, are those that indicate the original movement direction of the ice.

Where the bedrock of the glaciated valley floor is exposed, it will frequently show glacial **striations** (scratches) where glacial debris has been ground across the surface. These striations are useful in indicating the trend of the ice movement. If you feel glacial striations carefully with your fingertips, you can often detect that one direction is more smooth than the other. The ice moved in the smooth direction.

The bedrock is more resistant in some places than others and where parts of it were upstanding beneath the ice, the up-ice side will have become abraded to a smooth, shallow slope whereas plucking of the down-ice side will have produced a steeper, more irregular face (as shown in Figure 1.25). These features are called by their French-derived name, **roches moutonnées** and they, like striations, are also valuable in indicating ice-flow directions.

Meltout deposits

Like ice sheets, valley glaciers deposit terminal moraines wherever the snout of the glacier has been stationary for some time. These terminal moraines may act as dams across the valley floor. Valley glaciers also deposit ground moraine over the valley floor. The ground moraine can consist of three different types of till deposit: the till smeared onto the ground at the base of the glacier, followed by layers of till from within the melted ice, and then layers of the material that was being carried on the top of the ice. In addition these glaciers deposit mounds of till at the valley sides. Such deposits are called **lateral moraines** and are largely the accumulation of material that the glacier eroded from the side of the valley or that fell on to the top surface of the glacier from the valley sides, having been loosened by freeze–thaw action. At places where two glaciers met, their lateral moraines will have joined together near the centre of the valley to form a **medial moraine** of till. The actual position of the medial moraine on the valley floor depends on the relative sizes of the two glaciers that flowed together. Drumlins may be found on the valley floor as well.

Figure 1.25
Roche moutonnée formation.
Describe the features of glacial erosion you might expect to find on the up-ice side.

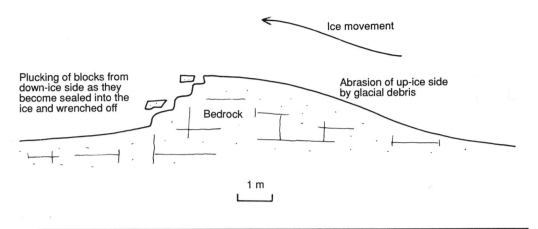

Meltwater deposits

The meltwater deposits from valley glaciers are very similar to those of ice sheets found in lowland areas, but are simply restricted by the sides of the valley. Thus braided stream sediments are common and kames and eskers may also be found. Long narrow **ribbon lakes** may form where a valley was dammed by a terminal moraine or where there was **glacial over-deepening**, i.e. deeper glacial erosion where bedrock was softer. The lakes become steadily filled with sediment. Material is either deposited by the in-flowing stream at the top end of the lake, building out a delta which eventually becomes a flood plain, or, if material is brought into the lake by a stream from the side, it can build out as an alluvial fan-delta deposit, possibly cutting the lake in two. A famous example of this is the separation of Buttermere from Crummock Water in the Lake District. Overall, deposition tends to smooth out the valley floor to form a flat alluvial flood plain drained by a meandering stream with ribbon lakes in places. These are vital agricultural areas in mountain regions such as the Alpine valleys of Switzerland and Austria.

The deposits that may be found in glacial valleys are summarised in Figure 1.26. These sediments are characterised by great variation in grain size, such as layers of boulders being sandwiched between beds of silt.

Recognising Continental Sediments

In comparison with coastal or deep-sea sediments, continental deposits are generally nearer their source, so tend to be less mature, more poorly sorted and more angular. This generalisation has a number of exceptions; dune sands, for example, are quite the opposite. However, dunes do contain large-scale cross-bedding, and since this is only usually formed by wind and on land, its presence normally indicates that these sediments were deposited on the continent.

The red coloration of sediments in deserts, produced because desert weathering causes iron to accumulate in its oxidised form, is another good indicator of continental conditions. Other features that form only on land are soils and their associated rootlet beds; ventifacts (by sand-blasting in deserts); striated glacial pebbles (although these could have been dumped at sea by floating ice sheets or icebergs) and certain fossils and trace fossils (of for example the dinosaurs, most mammals and their footprints). However, continental sediments are generally characterised by a lack of fossils since many continental environments where sediments form are not only poor environments for life but have poor preservation potential as well. In contrast, coastal and shallow marine sediments tend to have abundant signs of life.

Figure 1.26
A summary diagram of glacial and post-glacial deposits in glacial valleys.
How do glacial and post-glacial deposits differ from one another?

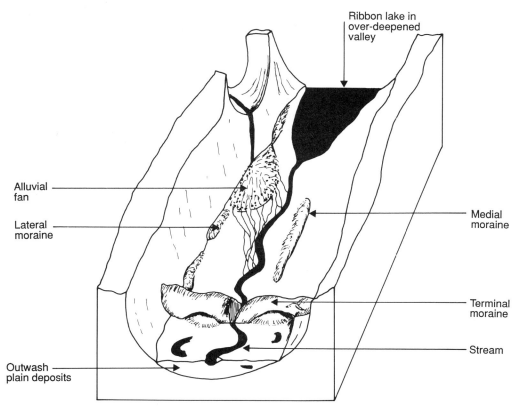

Economic Aspects

Diamond Prospecting in Ancient Braided Streams

Diamonds are found in an igneous rock called **kimberlite**. The kimberlite is emplaced (intruded into position) by a large-scale drilling process which brings it to the surface from great depth in the form of a vertical pipe. All diamonds either come directly from kimberlite or originated in kimberlite before being eroded and redeposited elsewhere.

Diamonds occur with other minerals that are characteristic of kimberlite, particularly a variety of deep red garnet. Since the garnets are much more numerous than diamonds, normal practice is to prospect for kimberlitic garnets and to hope that, when the source of these has been found, diamonds will also be found. Kimberlites seem to have a random distribution within the shields (the ancient Precambrian cores of many continents) of the world, particularly within the shield rocks of southern Africa, so prospecting needs to be carried out throughout any shield area where there have been previous reports of diamonds. Diamonds, garnets and other kimberlitic minerals are heavy, i.e. they have a higher relative density than most other minerals found in sediments. They therefore tend to accumulate with the coarser materials in streams. This fact is exploited in the initial search for sources of diamonds which consists of collecting large numbers of stream samples from the area being prospected. The samples are treated so that the heavy minerals can be removed. These are then analysed to discover if any kimberlitic minerals are present.

If kimberlitic minerals are discovered, another series of samples is taken in the mineral-rich stream to locate the point above which no further such minerals can be found. It must be from below this point in the stream valley that the minerals have come. Once this spot has been located, a soil sampling programme using a grid pattern is carried out in the areas beside the stream. This is to find the place in the soil where kimberlitic mineral concentrations are highest – a place called the **anomaly** or high point, searched for by all prospectors.

In the 1970s this sequence of events was carried out in an area of Swaziland. As a result a 1-kilometre-long, north–south trending kimberlitic mineral anomaly was found. Three of the many soil samples taken contained tiny diamonds. Finding diamonds in soil samples is highly unusual and this indicated that there was possibly an important diamond source nearby. A strip anomaly of this type would normally be produced by a kimberlite dyke, so trenches across the anomaly were excavated to find and evaluate the diamondiferous dyke. It was very surprising to find not kimberlite but instead a series of coarse Jurassic sandstones that contained the diamonds and kimberlitic minerals. This was very unusual because sedimentary rocks containing diamonds are almost unknown.

The sandstone deposit in this case was evaluated, but it was found not to be rich enough on its own to make a diamond mine. If there was to be a diamond mine, the source of the original diamonds had to be found. This was where the sedimentologists came in. Detailed studies of the sandstones showed that they were braided stream deposits. Palaeocurrent analysis showed that the ancient streams had flowed westwards. The source of the diamonds must therefore have been in the east. So, prospecting by stream and soil sampling was intensified towards the east and eventually the kimberlite source of the diamonds was found. This deposit is now being mined profitably for diamonds, the successful conclusion to a rather unusual prospecting story.

Placer Gold in South Africa

One of the most important gold-producing areas in the world is the Witwatersrand Basin in the Johannesburg region of South Africa. The gold is found there in Precambrian conglomerates. Palaeocurrent investigations reveal that these are gravels deposited by braided streams that drained the granitic shield rocks to the north of the area and swept south into the Witwatersrand Basin. The richest parts of the goldfield are the points where the streams first entered the basin forming gravel-filled channels. The gold, being very dense, was deposited in the channels with the gravels. These deposits are now the gold 'reefs' which are mined in the deepest mines in the world.

The Caithness Flags

The Caithness flags are a Devonian deposit which outcrops over much of the Caithness area in the extreme north-east of Scotland, underlying John o' Groats. The flags are fine, well-bedded sandstones which can easily be split into fairly thin sheets for flagstones. Caithness flagstones have, in times past, been transported to many areas of Britain for use as paving stones. The Caithness flag sequence also contains abundant ripple marks, cross-bedding and desiccation cracks. There are no marine fossils but fossil land plants are present. All these characteristics indicate that the sediments were deposited in a landlocked lake under semi-arid conditions. They are therefore fossilised Devonian playa lake deposits.

One very characteristic feature of the Caithness area is the field boundaries. Since timber is scarce and flagstones are common, the walls are made of upended flags placed side by side. These barriers, though unusual, are very effective.

Today, natural flagstones are rarely used for paving stones since manufactured concrete slabs are cheaper and much more common.

Marl and Marl Pits

Marl is clay or siltstone cemented with calcium carbonate and it is most frequently formed by the evaporation of lake sediments under arid conditions. Marls of Triassic age form a widespread deposit in the Cheshire Basin. Historically this has been of economic significance to farmers. Many areas of Cheshire are covered by heavy, impermeable glacial till deposits. These produce a poorly drained acid soil. The calcareous marl occurs beneath this soil, and so to reduce the soil's acidity and thus increase its fertility, many farmers in the past excavated marl pits and spread the marl over their fields. This is why today, thousands of small flooded marl pits are found dotted around Cheshire and surrounding areas. Farmers now purchase lime and other commercial fertilisers instead of using the traditional marl.

Sand and Gravel Deposits

The most important use for sand and gravel is as aggregate, i.e. a material used to add to cement to make concrete. Sand and gravel are heavy bulk materials to transport and their overall cost approximately doubles for every 30 kilometres of transport necessary. Thus, an essential feature for the exploitation of a sand or gravel resource is that it be sited near the area where it is needed. Most gravel pits are therefore found near large urban areas. Many of the deposits being worked in Britain today are glacial meltwater deposits. Examples include the deposits on the River Thames and the River Lune.

There are several key requirements that a sand or gravel resource must meet to be economically viable. The first is that the deposit should be fairly well sorted with virtually no silt and mud. The deposit must also be reasonably extensive and thick with a relatively thin soil cover that can easily be removed. As the excavated pits quickly flood, much of the material is removed by dredging, before being washed and sieved into various grain sizes.

Beware: working or abandoned gravel pits can be very dangerous places, with poorly consolidated banks and great irregularities on the floors of the pits. If you ever visit one, be careful.

Due to modern planning controls, gravel pits have now either to be reclaimed and landscaped after use, or turned into marinas, bird sanctuaries, or some other useful adaptation of the site.

Practical Investigation and Fieldwork

By carrying out the investigations described below you will develop your own understanding of sedimentary processes in action and gain a good insight into how sedimentary environments, and their associated characteristics, develop and operate.

Investigations 2–5 are all to be carried out in active sedimentary environments. Locations such as these, where sedimentary processes are operating, are dangerous by their very nature. Do take care during your studies in these places. Never go alone and always tell someone where you have gone and how long you expect to be away. Wear sensible clothing and footwear, and carry a whistle for emergency use.

1. How do braided and meandering streams develop?

Set up a **stream table**, or a tray filled with sand, dipping gently towards a sink. (A piece of guttering filled with sand is a good substitute.) Use rubber tubing to pipe water on to the top end of the table. After a few minutes fine braiding patterns will be seen to have developed in the sand. Observe the braiding process carefully. You will be able to note that channel-switching occurs when a channel becomes blocked by its own sediment. What are the processes that lead up to the development of the braid pattern? What shape is a braid bar? What controls the width of the braid pattern development?

Braided channels form naturally on a stream table; meandering channels do not develop as easily. When the sediment in the stream table has become waterlogged, use a dessertspoon to excavate a straight channel down the centre of the table as far as its lower end. The channel should be the width of the dessertspoon and its base the floor of the stream table. Add water to the top end of the channel and watch for the meandering process to begin. If meanders do develop, what appears to be the trigger?

How wide is the meander belt that forms? What cross-sectional shape does the channel develop? How does this relate to areas of erosion and deposition? If meanders do not develop, try again using different rates of water flow.

2. How do scree slope environments work?
Investigate an active (i.e. non-vegetated) scree slope in the manner described below.

a) Measure the slope angle and mean clast size at regular intervals (stations) along a transect (straight line) from top to bottom.
b) Measure the orientation of the long axes of randomly chosen clasts at stations down the transect. Use these measurements as a guide to whether clasts move in general by sliding, rolling or bouncing.
c) Observe the link between gullies in the free face and the positions of the tops of cones of scree (called talus cones).
d) Observe the avalanching process when the scree material is dislodged by your foot.
e) Calculate and plot the shape of the receding cliff edge in cross-section. Plot a graph of a vertical cliff of known height. Consider the collapse of a fixed thickness of cliff. Measure the cross-sectional area of the collapse and transpose it to a scree of the same cross-sectional area with a suitable slope (35°). Assume a percentage (e.g. 20 per cent) of coarse material accumulating at the foot of the slope and a similar percentage of finer material at the top. Plot the boundaries (which will be gradational) between the coarse, medium and fine sediment as dashed lines. Repeat the exercise for similar thicknesses of cliff face until all the free face is consumed.

The final model you produce may look like Figure 1.2 (see page 7).

(This investigation, and the three that follow, are based on King, 1984.)

3. How do braided streams and rivers work?
Carry out the following investigation for a braided stream. Such streams are largely found in upland areas of Britain, but meandering streams can show braided patterns in seasons of low flow.

a) Map a small area of the braided stream, identifying those channels that are highly active and comparing them with channels that are less active and those which are largely abandoned.
b) In an active channel measure and plot the profile (the shape of the cross-section) from bank to bank. Then plot the sediment size and the sedimentary structures onto the profile. Measure current flows and directions and add these to the profile. Finally, observe any active processes and note these observations on the profile as well.
c) Repeat (b) for a less active channel, recording your results in the same way.
d) Observe and assess the effect of vegetation on erosion and deposition in braid bars.

Use all the information you have collected to attempt to work out how the braided area will develop as sediment builds up. Try to draw a block diagram model to show your ideas. The final result might look like the one shown in Figure 1.6 (see page 12).

4. How do meandering streams and rivers work?
These are complex environments, but you can nevertheless gain an insight into how they develop by making careful observations as described below.

a) Map a small area of the flood-plain to show the major elements.
b) Make measurements in an active channel similar to those suggested for a braided stream channel in Investigation 3(b) above. Record your results in the same way.
c) In an abandoned channel dig small pits in dry areas to observe sediment size, structure and content of organic material. Then observe the conditions on the margins of parts of the abandoned channel that are still flooded.
d) Observe flood plain sediments in a cut bank. Record changes in sediment size and structure up the sequence.

Attempt to use all your observations to show how the meandering stream environment will develop over time. Work out the sequences that are likely to be preserved. Draw your conclusions together in a block diagram, like the one shown in Figure 1.14 (see page 19).

5. How do coastal dune environments work?

These are rather complex environments since wind directions vary and the baffling and binding effects of vegetation can be critical. However, you will understand the basic processes of dune development by undertaking the investigations described below.

a) Measure the angles of dip of steep (lee) slopes of dunes in order to determine the angle of rest of dry dune sand.

b) Measure the orientation of dune lee faces and the orientations of wind ripples to gain an idea of the major wind directions and any secondary flows or eddies that might exist.

c) Measure the sediment size and observe the sediment shape and sediment composition of the dunes. Do the same for an inter-dune area. Compare the two sets of observations. The differences that you note are the results of the different processes active in dune and inter-dune areas.

d) Observe the avalanching process as sand on a lee slope is dislodged.

e) Observe the different modes of sand movement on a windy day.

f) Measure dune height and percentage vegetation cover along a transect in order to establish any link between these two factors.

A model of a coastal dune environment, based on the types of observations you have been asked to make, is shown in Figure 1.27.

Figure 1.27
A model of the resultant sequence that might be produced in a coastal dune environment. Why do the cross-bed sets have many different orientations?

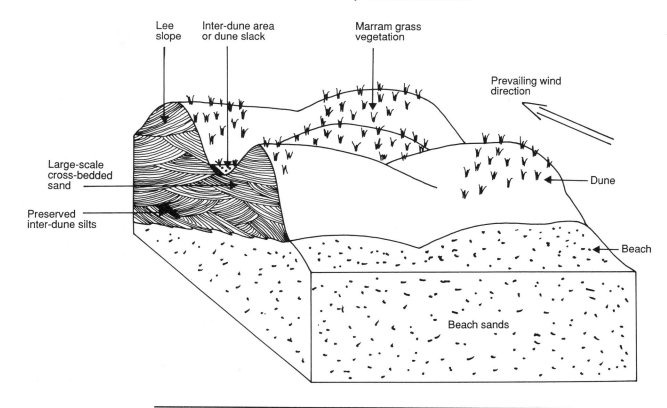

Test Your Understanding

1. Why are screes cone-shaped? What controls the cone angle?

2. An oil company prospecting for hydrocarbons has identified a potential oil prospect. Previous investigations have shown that there is a deep source of hydrocarbons and that a potential reservoir rock of fluvial sediments is present, capped by an impermeable clay in an anticlinal structure. Thus a source, a cap rock and a trap are present, but is the sandstone a good reservoir rock? The detailed sedimentology of the river deposit is unknown. Write a technical report for the oil company comparing braided and meandering stream sequences for their potential as reservoir rocks, assuming that no compaction or cementation has taken place. In your report, you should take into account that a good reservoir rock will have high primary porosity (which will be affected by grain size, sorting and packing), will be large in volume, will have few and scattered impermeable beds and will have channels or ducts through which the hydrocarbon can flow. In your conclusion, note which of the two sequences would be preferable according to the characteristics you have described.

3. Figure 1.28 shows stratigraphic logs that might be expected for braided and meandering stream sequences. Which is which? Explain the reasoning behind your answer.

Figure 1.28
Typical sequences that might be produced by braided and meandering streams. (Refer to the key given in Figure 1.8 on page 13.)

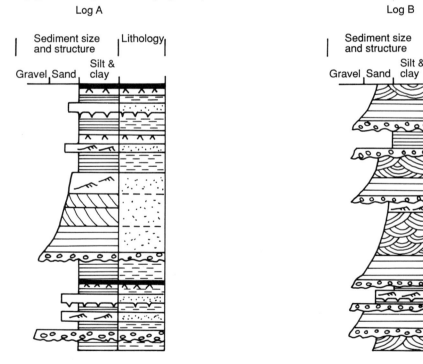

---

4. Where in braided and meandering stream sequences would you expect to find heavy minerals such as gold and tin ores concentrated? Explain your answer.

5. Much of the water supply of the Manchester area is pumped out of an aquifer which is Triassic in age. Where this aquifer outcrops, it shows many features of aeolian origin. Why are buried dune sands likely to make good aquifers?

6. Many of the Triassic sandstones in Cheshire are aeolian dune sands which have been reworked and redeposited by streams. How might their dune sand origin be established? What characteristics might indicate that they were redeposited by water?

7. Till deposits found down the east coast of England often contain shells of shallow marine and intertidal origin. These deposits are called shelly drift. What could account for the presence of these remains in glacial till?

8. In the past many Norfolk farmers excavated pits through the till deposits on their land to the chalk beneath. Why might they have excavated these pits?

9. Figure 1.29 shows a number of cores taken from glacial lake sediments. Attempt to correlate the varved sequences. Assuming that only one varve was produced per year, work out the age of the oldest varve. How long ago was the warmest summer?

Figure 1.29
Varved sediments taken from a number of glacial lakes.
The core on the far left-hand side was taken from a modern lake.

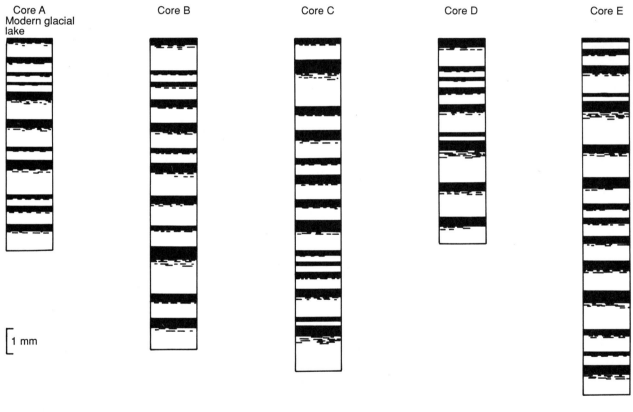

10. What features might enable you to distinguish braided stream sediments deposited in desert conditions from those deposited in glacial or periglacial conditions?

11. How might lacustrine sediment sequences from desert, temperate and periglacial lakes be distinguished?

12. Why are spores and pollen particularly important in Britain for correlating rocks of Devonian, Permo-Triassic and Pleistocene age?

2. DEPOSITION ON THE SHORELINE

Deposition on the shoreline can be caused by a variety of different processes. Some of these are physical, like wave and tidal processes. Some are chemical, like the laying down of sea salts by evaporation. Others are biological, such as the formation of reefs by corals and other organisms. Often, several of these processes work together to produce very varied depositional conditions. Of course other areas of shorelines are dominated by erosion; or deposition and erosion are in balance so that no sediment accumulates. The result of all these different processes is the tremendously varied shores that we find on the margins of lakes, seas and oceans today.

This chapter begins by examining coastal environments that are likely to be familiar to you, so that you can get a feel for the processes that are active through your own experience. The coastal environments that are less familiar, such as those in tropical and arid areas, are dealt with later in the chapter.

Beaches

Conditions of initiation
Beaches are produced by waves. Therefore the key condition of initiation for beach formation is a body of water large enough for waves to be formed by wind blowing over its surface. Thus beaches form on sea shores, and also on the shores of larger lakes. Where there are waves, there will be beaches; without waves, beaches do not form. A second condition of initiation is that the shoreline must be sloping. Where there are only steep cliffs, the sediment eroded by wave power is transported away and beaches do not develop. Instead the material is carried to lower energy, shallower slope areas where it is deposited. Thus, in regions where rock types of varying resistance are found the tougher rocks form steep headlands, whereas in the bays formed in the softer rocks, beaches develop. In areas of very shallow slopes, marshes or tidal flats develop instead of beaches.

Transportation and deposition of sediments
To understand the transportation and deposition of sediments by waves, we must first look at the water movement caused by wave action. The main movements, in cross-section, are shown in a series of diagrams in Figure 2.1.

The waves that develop in deep-water areas involve an up and down movement of the water surface. However, the water particles do not simply move up and down. The whole motion can be shown by the movement of a floating object, such as a cork (this movement can be seen particularly well in a wave tank in the lab). As the crest of the wave approaches the cork rises, but it is also moved forward in the direction that the wave is moving. As the crest passes and the wave trough approaches the cork falls, but

Figure 2.1
Water movement caused by waves as they approach the shore.
What would be the effects on a cork in the breaker, surf and pool zones?

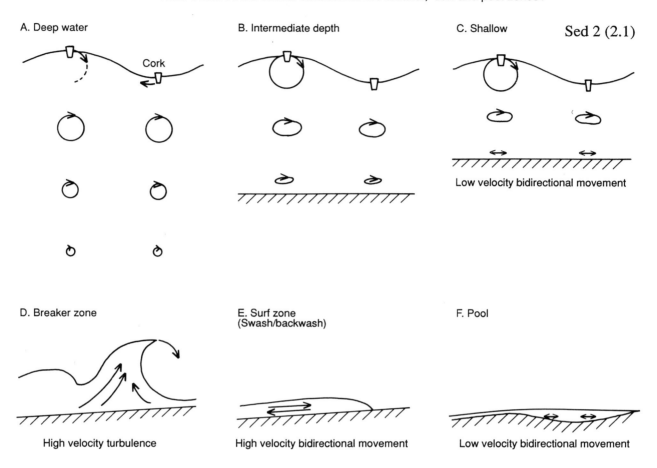

it also moves backwards. Altogether therefore, the cork actually has a circular motion. The water particles have the same circular motion as the cork. The power of the wave movement decreases with depth, so the water particles move in smaller and smaller circles until the water movement dies away all together. The depth at which the effects of the surface waves die away, i.e. the depth below which sediments cannot be moved by waves, is called the **wave base**. The most powerful storm waves can cause water movement down to around 200 metres depth, but waves like this are very uncommon and most waves cause water movement only to a depth of a few metres.

Where waves are moving towards a shoreline the water becomes shallower until the waves begin to 'feel' the bottom. When this happens the water particles can no longer move in a circular fashion, so the circles become squashed, as shown in Figure 2.1(B). At shallower depths still, only backward and forward water movement is possible (Figure 2.1(C)). It is when this backward and forward (i.e. **bidirectional**) water movement has a high enough velocity that sediments begin to be moved.

As the water becomes shallower still, the wave 'feels' the bottom more and more. The friction produced causes the lower levels of the water to move more slowly in the direction of the wave movement than the upper levels, so the higher levels of water therefore spill over to form a breaker (Figure 2.1(D)). In the breaker zone there is much high-velocity turbulent water movement, as you will know if you have ever been surfing. The breaker collapses to form a **bore** of water that is driven up the beach. In this surf zone (Figure 2.1(E)) the water movement up the beach is called **swash**. This is followed by **backwash** as the water drains back down the shore. Water movement is therefore again bidirectional and high velocities of water and sediment movement can occur in this zone. In some parts of the shoreline the swash may spill over into a shallow pool, again producing bidirectional movement, this time of a lower velocity (Figure 2.1(F)).

When waves are observed in plan view, they are seen to be lines of parallel wave crests 'marching' towards the shore. Since wind directions are rarely at right angles to the shore, the wave crests usually approach the shore obliquely. It is the shoreward part of a wave, therefore, that begins to feel the bottom first. The effect of this is shown in Figure 2.2. The shoreward part of the crest is slowed, causing the crest to curve to

Figure 2.2
Waves approaching the shore at an angle.
The waves are refracted but still produce saw-tooth water movement on the beach, resulting in longshore currents. Would longshore drift be greater on steep or shallow beaches?

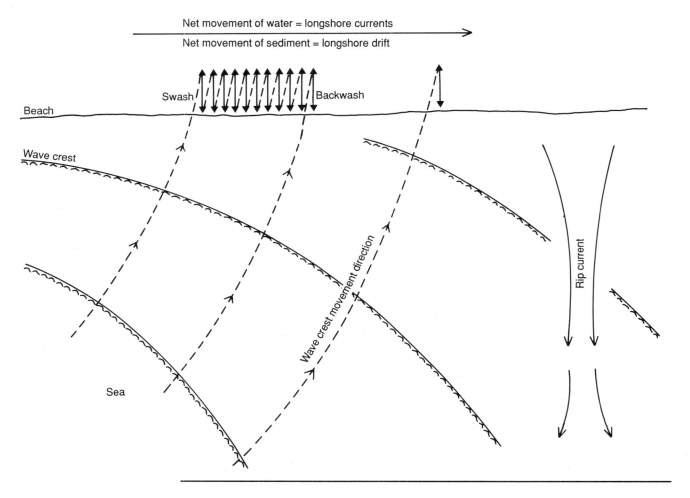

become more parallel to the shoreline. This is **wave refraction**. Despite this refraction, most waves still meet the shoreline at an angle so that the swash is driven up the beach at an angle. Since the backwash then drains straight down the slope of the beach, under the influence of gravity, the water is actually driven along the beach in a saw-tooth motion. The net movement of water along the beach produces **longshore currents** (i.e. currents along the shore) parallel to the beach. These longshore currents cause the sediment to move along the shore in a saw-tooth motion too. The net sediment movement along the shore is called **longshore drift**.

When the sand or shingle that is carried along by longshore drift reaches the end of the beach, deposition continues such that a bar of sediment is built out. This is called a **spit**. The growth of spits can have an important effect upon the geography of coastlines, and mouths of rivers can be deflected in the direction of the drift by hundreds of metres or even at times by kilometres. Such river deflection has occurred on the east coast of East Anglia, deflecting both the rivers Yare and Alde. The deflection of the Alde by the building of the Orford Ness spit is a very well known example (see Figure 2.3A).

Figure 2.3
Spits.
Orford Ness in East Anglia has deflected the mouth of the River Alde to the south by 13 kilometres. Spurn Head is a hooked spit that has developed on the northern shore of the Humber Estuary. Chesil Beach is a tombolo which now joins the Isle of Portland to the Dorset mainland. What were the directions of the wave and sediment movements that caused spit formation in each case?

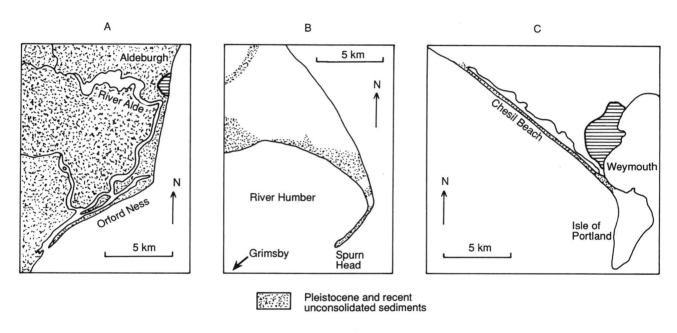

Pleistocene and recent
unconsolidated sediments

When refraction of waves occurs around the end of a spit, a **hooked spit** such as Spurn Head on the northern shore of the Humber Estuary develops (Figures 2.3B). Spits which build out to connect two headlands or connect an island to the mainland are called **tombolos**. One of the most impressive barrier beaches in Britain is Chesil Beach, which is a tombolo of shingle that connects the Isle of Portland to the Dorset coast (Figure 2.3C).

On beaches subject to longshore drift, the longshore water movement eventually breaks down and the water is carried back out to sea in powerful **rip currents** (see Figure 2.2). Rip currents form at right angles to the beach, and a hollow in the beach is often produced by the erosive power of the current. Unsuspected rip currents have caused many swimmers to drown. If you ever become caught in one remember that they are narrow currents, so swim sideways, along the beach, to escape. Surfers find rip currents useful because after they have caught a wave into the beach they can ride on a rip current back out to the breaker zone.

Longshore currents and rip currents are unidirectional, i.e. they flow in one direction, like river currents. Thus the same types of sediment transport and deposition, with their characteristic sedimentary structures, are produced in these currents as are found in rivers (see pages 8–10). However, in the shallow water areas before the breaker zone, in the swash and backwash and in the pool zones, bidirectional water movement occurs. The transportation and deposition produced by bidirectional water movement can be investigated in the laboratory in the same way that unidirectional water movement can be studied. A wave tank (see Figure 2.4) must be used which has a paddle to produce waves at one end and a means of absorbing the waves at the other end (otherwise the waves are reflected and bounce back to interfere with approaching waves).

Figure 2.4
A wave tank set up with a dipping base so that the waves are absorbed.
What different factors can change the power of the waves produced? (Wave power is a measure of the ability of the wave to do work, such as moving sediment.)

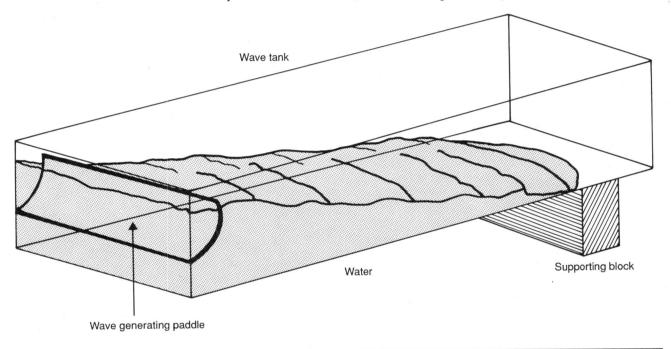

The results of investigations using a wave tank are shown in Figure 2.5. With a bed of medium sand, at low velocities of bidirectional movement, the sand grains are not moved or entrained. As velocities of water movement are increased, the grains begin to move to and fro over the whole bed. This whole bed movement soon breaks down to form a series of **symmetrical ripples** with crests parallel to the crests of the waves. The mode of formation of the ripples is shown in Figure 2.6. As the crest of the wave passes over the ripple, the sand moves up the side of the ripple in the direction of the wave crest movement, depositing a thin layer of sand. As the trough passes, the water moves backwards, causing sand to move up and deposit a layer on the other side of the ripple. Since both currents have the same power, the slopes are the same and the ripple remains symmetrical. As bidirectional velocities are increased, the rippled bed breaks down to form a flat or gently undulating **plane bed**.

If the same experiments are carried out with coarse sand a similar sequence of structures is produced, but at higher current velocities. Lower velocity currents can move finer sediment. Figure 2.5 has been built up by a series of experiments like these. Notice the similarity between this diagram and the one obtained for undirectional currents (see Figure 1.3, page 9).

Sediment types

When you used to visit the beach with your bucket and spade, you will have seen that beaches are usually made either of sand or of shingle (shingle is rounded beach gravel), but rarely a mixture of the two. You were then observing the sediment types that make

Figure 2.5
A graph of wave power against the sedimentary structures produced by waves in sediments of different grades. (From Allen, 1970.)
If the wave power were steadily increased, then steadily reduced, which type of sedimentary structure would be preserved?

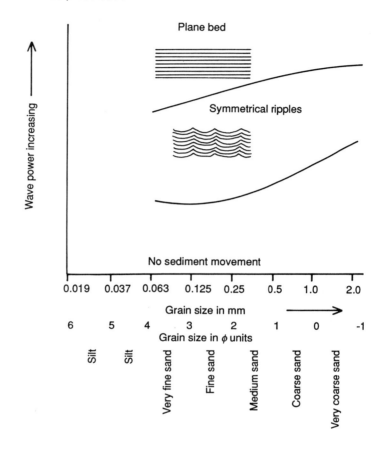

Figure 2.6
The formation of symmetrical ripples by wave action.
How would the water movements and their results change if the crest of the wave had been moving in the opposite direction?

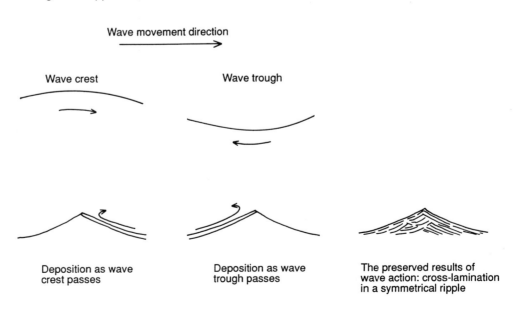

up beaches. Did you wonder why sands and shingles were rarely mixed? Did you wonder why beach pebbles were so smooth and rounded? The answers to these questions are linked to the tremendous amount of energy available in the continuously pounding waves.

Beaches in temperate regions are composed largely of clastic materials, i.e. sediment that has been eroded from pre-existing rocks. These rocks are usually those of the nearby headlands. After a cliff collapse on the headland, the fallen material is ground down and transported by the pounding waves such that boulders become broken down, pebbles become rounded and sands become well worn. The energy available from the ceaseless waves also sorts the sediment so that in high energy areas gravel (shingle) is deposited, and in moderate and lower energy areas sands are laid down. Since silts and clays can only be deposited in very low energy conditions, they are not normally found in beach environments. They are deposited by different processes elsewhere, such as on tidal flats or in the deep sea.

In tropical coastal areas where little clastic sediment may be available and much skeletal debris is produced by the abundant organisms, the beach sediments are made largely of carbonate (mainly calcium carbonate as aragonite and calcite). The carbonate sediments are also well worn and well sorted. Where there is no clastic sediment available, as on mid-oceanic islands for example, the pure white carbonate sand may squeak as you walk on it; so walking along a palm-fringed beach can be a squeaky experience.

Beaches around volcanic islands are often composed of black volcanic sand produced from eroded lava flows and pyroclastic deposits. These beaches are not so popular with the tourists!

Sedimentary structures

In addition to the true beach deposits, some coasts also have sand bars that form beyond the breaker zone, in the shallow sea area. These are rather complex structures formed by waves and by the longshore currents. They lie parallel to the beach and may be breached by the channels produced by rip currents. They are called **offshore bars**.

The whole shallow sea area beyond the breaker zone is affected by waves, and so symmetrical ripples are very common in this region. They become less common as the water becomes deeper and wave base approaches, and none at all are found below the wave base. If symmetrical ripples are preserved and examined in cross-section, the structure that is seen on the vertical surface is called **cross-lamination**. In the case of symmetrical ripples, this is symmetrical cross-lamination.

In the breaker zone, water velocities and turbulence are so great that sedimentary structures are destroyed rather than being formed. In the swash-backwash zone, by contrast, the surging bidirectional currents produce a relatively steeply dipping plane-bedded sequence in sands and shingle. It was in the area of damp flat sand formed by the swash-backwash zone that Robinson Crusoe saw his footprint. This is also the area where some of the best sand castles are made! The only place on the upper beach where ripples are likely to form is where pools cause low-velocity bidirectional currents to be formed again.

Other sedimentary structures that are commonly found on sandy beaches are those structures formed during draining, and afterwards when the sand is dry. As the water drains away, first **rill marks** (very small channels) then gullies can be formed. The water flowing over the surface of the beach or in the gullies is unidirectional, so current ripples can develop in these places. In fact, all the transitions between symmetrical wave ripples and asymmetrical current ripples are found on beaches. Water flowing across flat surfaces as they drain produces braided patterns in exactly the same way as braided streams (see page 8). Where this water runs into deeper pools, nicely formed micro-deltas develop. After drying out, tracks, trails, footprints and rain pits can be formed on the surface. With such variety possible, some beaches can be a veritable wonderland for geologists interested in sediments and sedimentary structures.

Although shingle may, as has been stated, have a coarse plane-bedded structure formed by the swash-backwash process, it is often structureless. The pebbles may however show the textural feature of imbrication (i.e. lying against each other like roofing slates). A ridge of shingle sometimes develops at the back of sandy beaches. This is called a **storm beach** and is produced during storms at high tide when the pounding waves are pushed higher up the beach than normal. A famous example is the storm beach at Newgale Sands in Pembrokeshire.

Fauna and flora

Shingle beaches contain very little fauna and flora because both life and preservation are difficult in the high energy environment. Sandy beaches in the area between tides are also fairly hostile to life. Few organisms can survive in an environment that can range between great extremes, which in this instance include the following: from under water (high tide) to dry (low tide); from hot (under the summer sun at low tide) to cool (under water at high tide); from frozen (in winter at low tide) to warm (under water at high tide); from violent conditions (during storms) to quiet conditions (on calm days), and from salt water (at high tide) to fresh water (during rain at low tide). However there are some organisms that have adapted to these conditions, usually by burrowing and/ or by preserving a more stable environment inside their shells. Sometimes such shelled organisms (e.g. cockles and razor shells) are preserved in the position in which they lived in beach sediments. Further off shore the environment becomes more and more stable, so life in various forms becomes more prolific and the preservation potential of these organisms is higher.

Most signs of life found on beaches, as you may well have seen for yourself, are tracks, trails and burrows of beach organisms. A variety of different shells may be found deriving from the beach itself, from off shore or from nearby rocky areas or tidal flats. The sea shells that you might have collected will usually have been the broken, worn, disarticulated remains of the more robust species, and these may be found scattered through the sand or in shell banks.

Geometry of the sediment body

The geometry of beaches in plan view is a strip of sediment parallel to the coast. Thus beaches, like some rivers, can form shoe string sands (see page 18). The difference between these two sand bodies is that while beaches parallel the coastline, river shoe strings form at right angles to the coastline. In cross-section, beach sediments may have a complex shape, possibly slab- or lens-shaped, sloping gently off shore. Structures in the sediment body, such as bars and ripples, generally run parallel to the shore and, when preserved, can be important indicators of the trend of the palaeo-coastline.

Resultant sequence

The resultant sequence preserved in beaches that are building upwards is shown in Figure 2.7. A transect across a beach area from sea to shore shows a general coarsening in the sediment, which is particularly emphasised where a storm beach has developed. This is because waves become generally more powerful and capable of moving sediment of larger size as they move on shore. As beaches build up by the accumulation of sediment over time, the sea is moved back. Thus the beach zones migrate seaward as deposition continues. The eventual effect is seen in Figure 2.7. In vertical sequence the finer offshore sediments coarsen upwards, possibly being capped by a storm beach deposit. The coarsening-upward sequence is associated with a change in sedimentary structures and a reduction in the number of organisms preserved. These features can be used to recognise coarsening-upward beach sequences in the fossil record.

Examples in the British Isles

Some of the Devonian sediments of North Devon show the features characteristic of beach environments, as described above. In the complicated shore zone that developed in that area in Devonian times, tidal flat, lagoonal and also river and deeper sea sedimentary environments formed.

Beach sediments are also preserved in the raised beaches of several parts of the coast of Scotland. After the disappearance of the ice at the end of the Pleistocene, the coast

Figure 2.7
The sequence of sediments produced by the building upwards and outwards of a beach environment.
The sediments coarsen upwards. How are other textural features of the sediment, such as rounding, sorting, packing, etc., likely to change up the sequence?

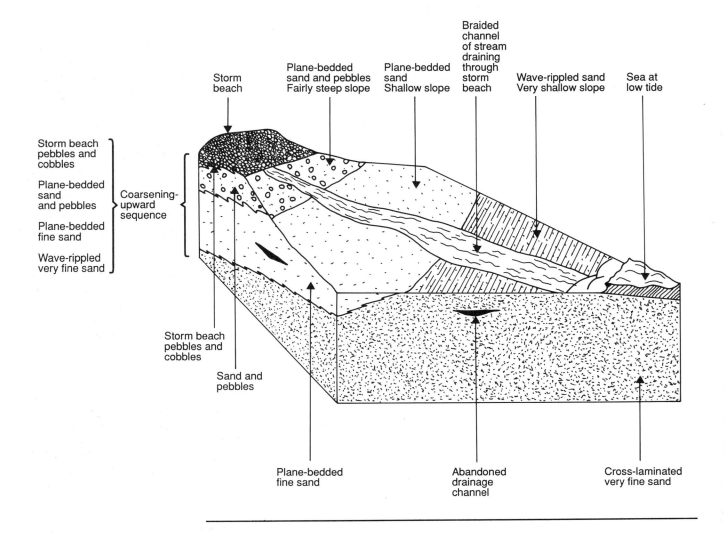

rose isostatically (i.e. as a bounce back effect after the removal of the weight of the ice). Wave-cut platforms and cliffs as well as beaches are now preserved several metres above sea level.

Tidal Flats and Estuaries

Conditions of initiation

Tidal flats form in **intertidal** areas (i.e. between the high and low water mark) which are not dominated by waves. The waves are kept out either by a very gently shallowing coastline (in which case the waves affect only the seaward edge of the tidal flat) or by a barrier such as a sandbank, spit or reef. Thus the conditions of initiation are tides with no waves. These conditions are found in many low-lying coastal areas in temperate regions and also in tropical and arid parts of the world. Arid tidal flats will be examined later in this chapter (see page 63). Tidal flat conditions also occur on the top surfaces of deltas, as is described on page 51.

Estuaries are special cases of tidal flats. They are normally **rias**, i.e. the drowned lower courses of river valley systems caused by the rising eustatic (world-wide) sea levels following the end of the Pleistocene glaciations. Waves attack only the mouths of the estuaries, leaving tides to dominate most of the rest of the area. The rivers that flow into the estuaries still bring in some sediment but they are not very important as sediment producers and transporters as their power has been reduced by the rise in sea level. However, the brackish water produced by the mixing of river and sea water causes **flocculation** of the fine suspended clays. This means that small individual clay particles clump together to form larger particles which settle at faster rates. Thus clays that might not otherwise be deposited are laid down in the lower-energy parts of estuary areas.

Transportation and deposition of sediments

Tidal processes are the dominant agents of transportation and deposition in tidal flat and estuarine areas. Tides are the rising and falling of water that produce little effect in the open sea but, when magnified by a shallowing coastline, can produce changes in water level as great as the 18-metre tidal range of the Bay of Fundy in eastern Canada. The tidal water movement is caused by the gravitational pull of the sun and the moon. As the Earth rotates beneath the moon, the moon pulls the Earth's water causing a tidal bulge; a similar bulge is produced on the opposite side of the Earth. Thus two bulges affect each part of the Earth every day. Twice each day the tide **floods** (flows in) to produce a **high tide**, and then **ebbs** (flows out), producing a **low tide** (though in fact, as the two high tides are a little more than 12 hours apart some areas may have only one high tide in a 24-hour period). This simple situation can be complicated in some places by the time it takes for water to flow to different parts of the region. This is the case around the Isle of Wight, where the same tide comes in from different sides of the island. Since the distances to be travelled around the island are different, one tide actually produces two high tides.

On this daily tidal cycle is superimposed a monthly cycle caused by the orbiting of the moon around the Earth. This is shown in Figure 2.8. The pull of the moon is much greater than that of the sun, but the sun does have some effect, such that when the sun and moon are pulling in the same direction, higher than normal high tides and lower than normal low tides are produced. These are called **spring tides**. The same thing happens when the sun and moon are on opposite sides of the tidal bulge. Spring tides therefore occur twice a lunar month. In between spring tides the sun and moon pull in opposite directions, causing a reduced effect on the tidal bulge. These tides are called **neap tides**, during which water does not move very far up or very far down beaches and tidal flats. Figure 2.9 shows the tidal predictions, including those for neap and spring tides, for Milford Haven in May 1979.

Tidal currents sweep onto the tidal flat during the flood tide, eroding channels and carrying sediment into the tidal area. Sand is swept up channels and finer sediments are carried in the shallower water over flats themselves. At high tide, when the water currents slow down and turbulence decreases, the main depositional process on the flats takes place: the fine silts and muds settle from suspension to form a thin blanket of fine sediment over the surface. As the water drains slowly from these surfaces on the ebbing tide, the sediment remains.

Sediment types

The main sediments found on tidal flats are the silts and muds deposited by settling. Sands are found on the offshore margins of the flats and in channels, where lag gravels may also be found. Since only fine sediment is laid down by settling, the sediments on the flat are well sorted. The channel sands are also well sorted because they are eroded and deposited four times a day, by the two flood and two ebb tides.

Sedimentary structures

The most common sedimentary structure formed in the tidal flat area is the lamination caused by the layer by layer deposition of the settling sediment. This fine structure is, however, often destroyed by the prolific burrowing organisms that live there. This churning up by burrowers is called **bioturbation**. When the flats dry out desiccation

Figure 2.8
Spring and neap tides caused by the gravitational pull of the moon and the sun.
Why does the moon have a greater pull than the sun?

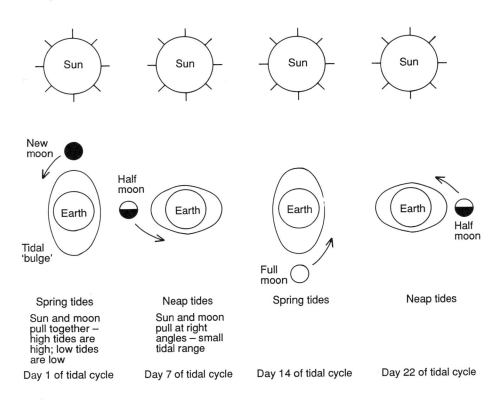

Figure 2.9
Tidal predictions for Milford Haven, south-west Wales in May 1979.
These predictions may have been wrong. Why?

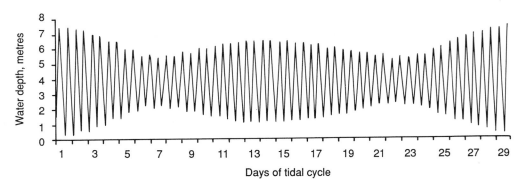

cracks often develop, particularly in the mud areas only covered during spring high tides. Tracks, trails, footprints and rain pits may also be formed on the surface.

The channels are affected by unidirectional currents four times a day. Two of these flows are inward and two are outward along the channels. The channels meander and so exactly the same processes are found as in meandering streams. However, such things as meander migration may happen faster in tidal channels, due to the four flows a day, unless the mud banks are sufficiently strong and cohesive to resist erosion. The channels contain the sedimentary structures typical of meandering streams.

Fauna and flora

The mud flat environment provides good conditions for life, with its low energy and 'rain' of sediment and food at high tide, so many organisms have adapted to living there. The main problem, that of drying out during tides, is countered by burrowing and by shell protection. Life in tidal flats is prolific, with large numbers of individual animals and a reasonable variety of species. Fewer species have adapted to the brackish water found in estuaries, but the numbers of individual organisms found there are just as great. In the shifting sands of the channels, few organisms live or are preserved, although the lag gravels may be composed of shell debris.

On the higher parts of tidal flats **halophytic** (salt-loving) plants can grow. These play a very important part in slowing down (**baffling**) the water movement around them, allowing sediment to settle at faster rates, and then **binding** the sediment with their roots. As a result of these baffling and binding processes, deposition in the areas colonised by plants is faster than elsewhere, causing the flats to build up more rapidly in these areas.

A plant that has been particularly effective in causing tidal flat growth is *Spartina*. The *Spartina* was developed experimentally in the 1950s to solve the problem of shifting mud banks in Southampton Water. A strain of *Spartina* was developed with good binding root systems which could only reproduce by putting roots out sideways, i.e. it did not produce fertile seeds. This was necessary to stop its spread to other parts of the world. It was very effective in Southampton Water, greatly reducing channel dredging costs. Unfortunately it soon evolved a fertile seed-producing mechanism and so has now spread to many of the tidal flat areas of Britain and Europe and also, recently, America. Thus tidal flats and estuaries that were once sandy have become fast-building muddy salt marsh areas. Fortunately, many Scottish estuaries are beyond the range of *Spartina* at present and so still support a wide variety of the specialised plants that have been ousted by *Spartina* elsewhere. In fact, Scottish tidal flat reeds are now exported to England for use as roof thatching.

Geometry of the sediment body

The geometry of tidal flats is that of broad areas that build up and out fairly fast to produce relatively thick deposits. The sediment bodies produced are thus flat and slab-like. In estuaries, the sediment bodies are confined by the funnel shape of the estuary shoreline.

Resultant sequence

In tidal flat areas wave and tidal power becomes reduced as the water approaches the land. This results in the sediments becoming finer the nearer they are to the land. Zones of sand, mud and marsh mud with their associated structures and organisms can be identified, running parallel with the coastline, as shown in Figure 2.10. These zones are crossed, roughly at right angles, by the channel systems. Tidal flats are often one of the areas of fastest deposition on the coast. As they build up, the sea is pushed back so that eventually the land is reclaimed naturally. Many of the low-lying coastal fenlands of Britain and Europe have formed in this way.

As the flats build up and out the zones move seaward, as shown in in Figure 2.10. The eventual result is that a fining-upward sequence is produced, which varies from wave-deposited sand to marsh mud – with related changes in structures and organisms. The thickness of the sequence produced depends on the tidal range: where tidal ranges are high, thick tidal flat sequences develop. All these characteristics can be used to recognise tidal sequences of the past.

Examples in the British Isles

Tidal sequences have been recognised in parts of the lower Silurian of the Welsh borderland and the middle Silurian of south-west Wales. During the lower Tertiary a low-lying shoreline crossed south-east England. To the north-west of this area, river sediments were deposited, while in the south-east normal marine sediments were laid down. In the area in between, extensive tidal flats and estuarine deposits were formed, with the characteristics described above. The shoreline migrated backwards and

Figure 2.10
The sequence of sediments produced by the building upwards and outwards of a tidal flat environment.
How would the tidal flat sequence produced in a tropical arid region differ from this?

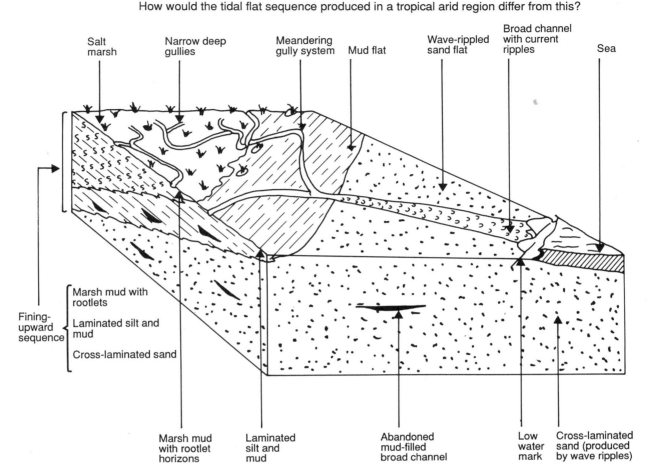

forwards over the region several times in response to eustatic (world-wide) changes in sea level. As a result, belts of tidal flat sediments are found in different places at different times in the sequence.

Deltas

Conditions of initiation

Deltas are not very common along the shorelines of the world, but when they do form, tremendous volumes of sediment can often be deposited. They form when a current of water carries sediment into a deeper, relatively still area, causing the sediment be deposited. Another important condition of delta initiation is that the sediment must not be removed (e.g. by tidal or longshore currents) at a faster rate than it is being deposited. Deltas can be formed on the edges of puddles, pools, ponds, lakes, seas or oceans. The small structure formed in the first three cases is called a **micro-delta,** and is produced by processes very similar to those that operate to form macro-deltas. Streams and rivers carry the sediment that builds deltas into lakes, seas and oceans. Generally, the greater the volume of sediment carried, the faster the growth of the delta. Deltas produce a bulge in the shoreline. In cases where sediment is removed faster than it builds out, either a straight coastline or an indented, estuarine coast forms instead.

Transportation and deposition of sediments

The general transportation and deposition processes are similar for all deltas: all major deltas are affected by the river that brings in the sediment and by the waves and tides of the sea area in which the delta is built. However, delta shape and type are greatly affected by whichever of these processes is dominant, and thus river-, wave- and tide-dominated deltas can be recognised.

The general process involves deposition by the river as it enters the relatively still, deeper water of the sea. The coarser material is deposited first and the finer sediment is carried further out before settling to the bottom. The coarse material piles up until it becomes unstable, at which point it either slumps or is carried down to produce a sloping **delta front** (see Figure 2.11). As this continues, a fairly flat surface to the delta builds out, called the **delta top** or **delta plain**. Meanwhile, the finer sediment has been carried beyond the sloping delta front to form a deeper deposit with a shallower gradient at the foot of the delta. This is the **pro-delta**. Pro-delta sediments are silts and muds. Delta front sediments are mainly sands and silts. On the delta top, gravels, sands, silts and muds can be deposited, depending on the circumstances.

Figure 2.11
A delta in cross-section.
What is the maximum possible slope of the delta front sediments?

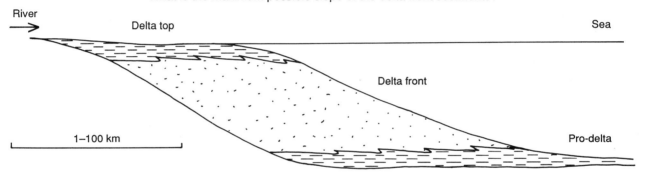

In deltas dominated by rivers, the body of water which receives the sediment is quiet. The river will have meandered across a low-lying plain, and these meandering characteristics continue out over the delta top unhindered. In this way the channels meander across the delta top, depositing lag gravels and point bar sands within the channels themselves. Levées form on the margins of the channels, with flood plain deposits beyond. At the edge of the delta top the channels continue to build out, eventually forming a large 'finger' of sediment. A number of channels, called **distributaries** (because they disperse the water from the river), build out a series of fingers to produce the typical **bird-foot** shape of river-dominated deltas. The fingers seen on the surface are just the top surface of large fan-shaped volumes of sediment called **delta lobes** (see Figure 2.12).

The 'flood plain' areas between the channels are called **interdistributary bays** since they are connected with the sea. Many of the sediments in these areas are reworked and redeposited by tides and have great similarities with tidal-flat as well as with flood-plain sediments. As sediment builds up on the floors and levées of distributary channels, the channels rise above the surrounding mud flats. Eventually, during a flood or storm, a levée is breached, water flows through at high velocity forming a crevasse, and a new channel develops. The new channel will build out a new finger over a new delta lobe, and so the process will continue. This natural process of channel switching is called **avulsion**.

Figure 2.12
*Delta growth and the avulsion caused by channel switching as deltas build into quiet water areas,
shown particularly well by the seven delta lobes built by the Mississippi over the last 5,000 years.
(After Kolb and Van Lopik, 1958 and Coleman 1976; in Leeder, 1982.)*
What are the likely characteristics of the coastal area near New Orleans today?

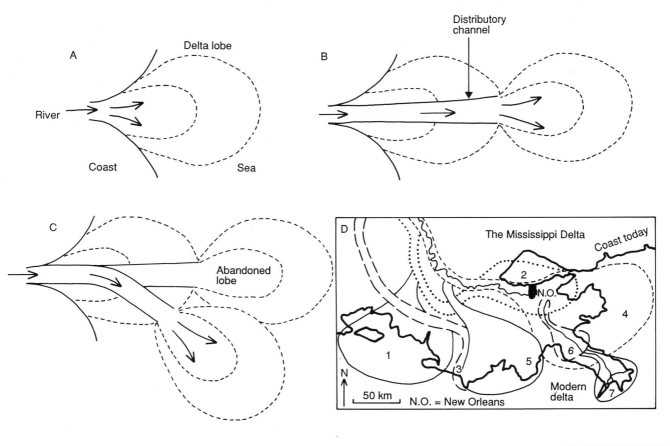

The Mississippi delta is the best-known example of a bird-foot delta. Seven major delta
lobes, each produced by a channel system rather than by individual channels, were
formed during the Holocene. The Mississippi River carries a huge volume of sediment
which is deposited in the quiet Gulf of Mexico to produce one of the largest deltas to
be forming on Earth today.

In areas where waves are dominant, the waves pick up and redeposit the sand and gravel
in a series of beaches and bars along the margin of the delta top. The outer margin of
the delta so formed is gently curved and, since many deltas develop in funnel-shaped
river mouths, the overall delta deposit is roughly triangular (see Figure 2.13). It is this
shape which has given deltas their name (the Greek capital letter 'delta' is a triangle).
The best-known deltas of this type are the Nile delta on the coast of northern Egypt and
the Niger delta formed where the north-trending coast of western Africa bends
suddenly westward.

Deltas dominated by tides look rather like a series of estuaries since the tidal currents
produce large funnel-shaped channels as they ebb and flow between large masses of
sediment. Well-developed bars form parallel to the tidal-movement directions on the
delta front. The best known of the tidally-dominated deltas is the Ganges-Brahmaputra
delta that has formed near Calcutta on the border between India and Bangladesh (see
Figure 2.13).

Figure 2.13
The Nile delta, a wave-dominated delta, and the Ganges-Brahmaputra delta, a tide-dominated delta. (From Selly, 1976.)
How would you expect the characteristics of the shorelines of the two deltas to differ from one another?

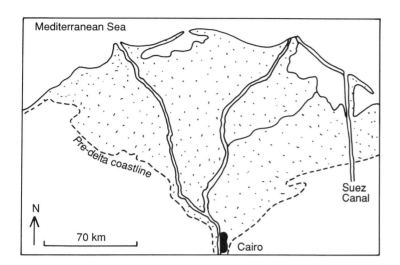
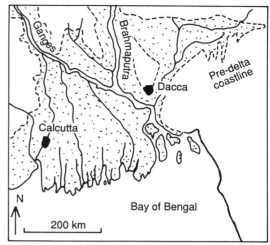

Sediment types
The sediment types associated with different parts of the delta are largely clastic, having been brought into the area by rivers. They tend to be fairly well sorted and their sizes range from the silts and muds of the pro-delta through the sands and silts of the delta front to the gravel and mud variation of the delta top.

Sedimentary structures
The sedimentary structures found the different parts of deltas are very similar to those described for other environments. As the delta top or plain is similar to flood plains and tidal flats, lamination, bioturbation and desiccation cracks together with tracks, trails and rain pits are found in the muds. Colonisation by vegetation may also produce rootlet beds or soil profiles. In the channels, cross-bedded lag gravels and sands are found together with plane bedding and various types of ripples.

The delta front is a rather complex environment dominated by the settling of sand, silt and some mud from suspension. Much of this is reworked by waves and/or tidal currents so that a variety of structures, from bars and dunes to ripples and flat bedding are produced. When seen in cross-section therefore, various types of bedding, cross-bedding, cross-lamination and lamination are seen, although bioturbation may remove all bedding traces. Slumping is also characteristic of this unstable area of fast deposition and relatively steep slopes, so slump scars are common, and a variety of slump features are found in the sediments.

The finer sediment of the pro-delta is usually laminated and may be bioturbated but other types of sedimentary structure are uncommon, due to the depth of deposition.

Fauna and flora
On the delta top the fauna and flora range from normal marine types at the outer marine to fresh-water types where river water flows into the area. They are similar to the organisms found in tidal flat, estuarine and flood-plain environments. However, one important addition is the luxuriant vegetation that can develop on delta plains in tropical regions. Mangroves are the only type of tree in existence today that are halophytic (i.e. can tolerate normal marine and brackish water). As a result they are prolific in these areas and create mangrove swamps with an ecology of their own.

Similar situations have arisen in the past. During the Carboniferous, for instance, forested swamps that were largely fresh water developed on delta tops, eventually producing the coals that are found in many parts of the world today.

Delta front and pro-delta sediments contain a variety of marine organisms but the environment, with its rain of sediment in murky water, is not ideal for life. Thus, even though preservation potential is good under these circumstances, organisms are not commonly preserved, and those that are to be found are greatly 'diluted' by the rain of sediment. Exotic remains, particularly of plant materials swept in by river and tidal currents, are fairly common in these beds. Some of these remains may be swept several hundreds of kilometres out to sea.

Geometry of the sediment body

Delta geometry is seen in cross-section in Figure 2.11 (page 51) and in plan view in Figures 2.12 (page 52) and 2.13 (page 53). Such deltas can be of various sizes, from the small bodies found in some lakes to deltas the size of the Mississippi, which has a surface area above water of 29,000 km^2. The Mississippi delta sediments are also enormously thick – up to 12 kilometres. This is because, although the active upper part of the delta is only up to 90 metres thick (as in other deltas), continued subsidence over the past 60 million years has resulted in a great sediment build-up.

Resultant sequence

Deltas are strongly depositional areas and so, like beaches and tidal flats, they build out and up over time, as is shown in Figure 2.14. As the delta front builds out over the pro-delta a coarsening-upward sequence is produced which may be capped by the even coarser sands and lag gravels of the distributaries (but may also be capped by interdistributary-bay muds). Thick, coarsening-upward sequences with their related structures and organisms, are thus characteristic of deltaic sequences and have often been used to identify such sequences preserved in the geological record.

Figure 2.14
The coarsening-upward sequence produced by delta growth.
How is this grain-size change related to energy levels during deposition in the different parts of the delta?

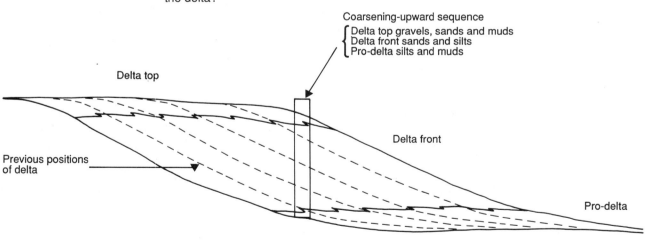

Examples in the British Isles

A good example of a deltaic sequence is found in the Peak District of Derbyshire. Here a turbidite fan deposit develops upwards into a series of coarsening-upward delta front sands and silts capped by coarse grits of delta-top channels. The resultant sequence is shown in Figure 3.17 (see page 96). It was on the tops of deltas such as these that the Carboniferous coal sequences developed.

A second good example of deltaic facies (i.e. the series of sediments deposited in a deltaic environment) is found in the middle Jurassic of the Yorkshire area. Here, three deltaic/fluvial cycles are recognised, with deltaic sediments coarsening upwards to the river flood-plain sediments preserved at the top. In these flood-plain sediments, desiccation cracks, dinosaur footprints and plants in upright positions are preserved.

Reefs, Carbonate Banks and Lagoons

The main carbonate-producing areas of the world are the shallow seas off palm-clad tropical island paradises and tropical coastlines that you may have seen on the television or even experienced yourself. Large volumes of calcium carbonate sediments can be formed in these conditions. Deposits like this in the past have formed the extensive limestones that we find in the geological record world-wide.

Conditions of initiation

Most of the calcium carbonate in these environments is produced by organisms. These, therefore, are the 'workers' in the carbonate 'factories' that can produce such large volumes of material. The prolific life necessary to produce these major accumulations can only occur in normal marine conditions where there is plenty of warmth, light, food and oxygen. The necessary warmth is found only in tropical and sub-tropical areas. Sunlight cannot penetrate murky seas, so the seas must be clear of clastic muds. The wave and tidal currents that bring food and oxygen into the area are found only in shallow waters. Thus tropical and sub-tropical clear shallow seas are necessary. Today such conditions are found in tropical and sub-tropical regions in the shelf areas off low-lying coastlines and around oceanic islands.

Limestones do form in other circumstances as well, but they are seldom very thick or extensive.

Transportation and deposition of sediments

The processes of sediment production, transportation and deposition differ in different parts of the shelf/coastal area and a number of sub-environments are recognised. These are summarised in Figure 2.15. The open sea shelf is below the wave base and so the type of sedimentation active here is very similar to the sedimentation in deep-sea areas which is described in Chapter 3 (page 81). Fine-grained laminated muds are the main deposit.

Figure 2.15
Depositional environments in carbonate areas.
Why have channels through barriers caused so many shipwrecks in the past?

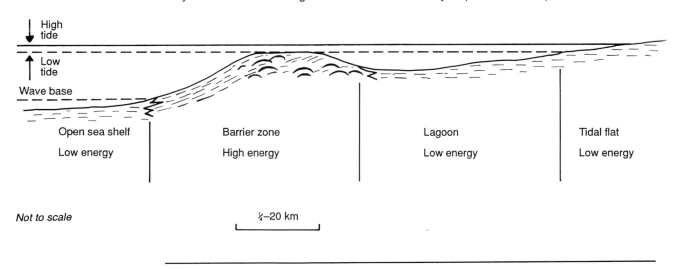

Not to scale   ¼–20 km

Barriers develop in most tropical shelf-sea environments. These are composed of reefs, sandbanks, small islands, or a combination of these. The barriers absorb the energy of the waves from the open sea, and tidal currents can only flow through gaps in the barriers. The lagoonal area behind the barrier is thus protected from waves and has only restricted tidal flows, making it a generally low energy environment.

In reef barriers of today, the framework is built mainly of coral and **calcareous algae**. Algae are simple plants and calcareous algae precipitate aragonite in their cells, their cell walls or around their cells. Thus, in the same way as corals build reefs by precipitating aragonite, so the aragonite precipitation of the algae can contribute to the reef-building process. Large numbers of other organisms are also part of, or live in, the reef structure. In the geological past, reefs of organisms other than coral, such as various types of algae, sponges, bryozoans, etc., also provided barriers to lagoons.

The structure of a reef is shown in Figure 2.16. The main structure is composed of dead coral with living coral on upper and outer surfaces. Corals at the front of the reef are tough and massive, to resist pounding by waves, but despite this a talus or scree slope

Figure 2.16
Reef structure and depositional environments.
How would a rise in sea level affect the reef?

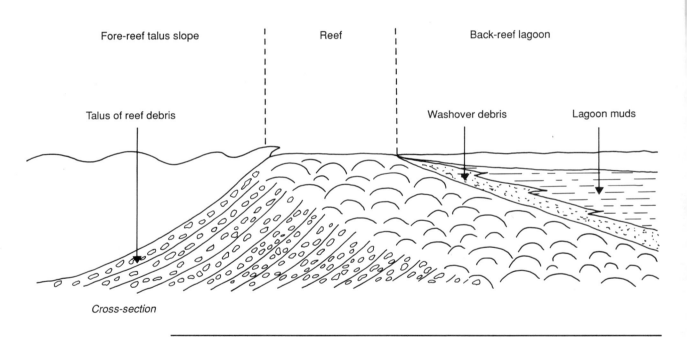

Cross-section

of reef debris develops down the reef front. The talus is composed of dipping beds of broken and abraded reef material. Some reef debris is swept over the reef into the edge of the lagoon during storms. Beyond the reef, on the edge of the lagoon, the more fragile corals and other organisms can grow. Patch reefs of similar corals often form within the lagoon as well.

The tidal currents that sweep to and fro through gaps in reef barriers reduce much of the reef debris to **skeletal sands** (i.e. sands made from the fragments of organisms), which develop the sedimentary structures such as cross-bedding and asymmetrical ripples that are characteristic of unidirectional currents. These sands tend to build out delta-like structures at both ends of the channels. The 'delta' at the lagoonal end is produced by flood tides, and the 'delta' at the open sea end of channels is built by ebb tidal flows.

Where reefs are not present, oolitic sandbanks can form barriers instead. Like the reefs, these sandbanks are subject to wave and tidal influence, so are formed into delta-like structures, sand bars, dunes, ripples, etc. Oolitic sandbanks showing all these structures have developed off the Bahamas, producing lagoonal environments within the sand barriers. Oolitic sandbanks also develop at times in the back-reef areas directly behind reef barriers.

The low energy of the lagoonal areas contrasts with the active reef and carbonate sandbank environments. Due to the low energy and the abundant food and oxygen supplies in much of the lagoonal area, life is prolific. You may well have seen television programmes showing the variety of brightly-coloured living organisms that thrive in this type of environment. The floor of the lagoon contains some patch reefs, but much of it is composed of carbonate sands, silts and muds. These are formed largely by the breakdown of organic material, particularly algae.

Some of the lagoonal areas are so wide that waves are generated within the lagoon, thus minimising the effects of the barriers. In these broad shelf areas, higher energies occur, so sediments are coarser and more subject to the sorting and abrasion caused by currents of various types.

Sediment types

Many of the sediment types found in carbonate depositional areas have been mentioned above. The four major types are: skeletal sands, oolitic sands, carbonate mud and pelleted mud (see Figure 2.17).

Figure 2.17
Carbonate sediments.
Skeletal sands and ooids have polished surfaces; pellets and grapestone do not. Explain this difference.

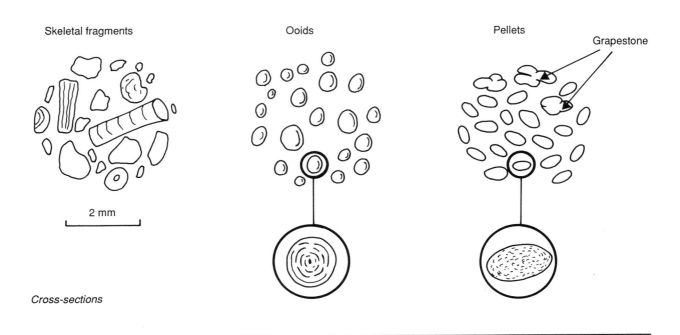

Skeletal sands are a major component of all carbonate environments. These **bioclastic** sands (composed of fragments of organisms) are formed not only of coral remains but also of the broken and worn fragments of many of the other reef-dwelling organisms that contain carbonate. Some of the important sand-producers of today and of the past include corals, gastropods, bivalves, brachiopods, crinoids, echinoids, stromatoporoids, foraminifera, bryozoa and various types of calcareous algae.

The **ooids** that make up **oolitic sands** are tiny balls of aragonite, from 0.1 to 1.5 millimetres in diameter, with shiny polished surfaces. They form where sea waters are agitated by waves or tides and where there is strong evaporation. Each ooid has a nucleus of a skeletal fragment or pellet around which concentric layers of aragonite have grown. This growth is aided by the presence of an organic film on the outer surface and by strong evaporation of the sea water which helps the precipitation of the calcium carbonate. Both the rounded shape and the polish of the surface are caused by the movement of the particles by the water currents. Ooids found preserved in the geological record are made of calcite and have a radial structure. Aragonite is unstable over geological time, and it is thought that the concentric aragonite structure breaks down to form the radial calcite ooids found in ancient limestones.

The very fine **carbonate mud** found on the floors of lagoons is composed of fine aragonite needles. These are largely produced by the breakdown of calcareous algae. Sometimes aragonite needles can also be formed by strong evaporation of the sea water which causes the calcium carbonate to precipitate out in this form. After crystallisation, the needles settle to the floor of the lagoon. It is this fine aragonite mud which, after diagenesis, becomes the microcrystalline **micrite** that forms many fine-grained limestones.

Many organisms, such as small gastropods, bivalves and worms, live in the carbonate mud of the lagoon floor and feed by chewing their way through this mud, which contains nutrients. The unwanted carbonate is excreted as faecal pellets. These are oval and range from 0.1 to 3 millimetres in length. Much of the carbonate mud is completely pelletised in this way. These **pellets** sometimes become clumped together into lumps which are called **grapestone**, for obvious reasons (see Figure 2.17, page 57).

In preserved limestone sequences the larger grains (skeletal fragments, ooids or pellets) are bound together either by a matrix of carbonate mud that filled the gaps between the grains during deposition (which later changed during diagenesis into fine micrite), or by a coarse calcite cement. The calcite cement, called **spar**, will have been deposited in the gaps between the grains by pore waters during diagenesis.

Sedimentary structures

The only sedimentary structures associated with reefs, apart from the reef structure itself, is the steep bedding – up to about 20° – associated with the reef talus. The skeletal and oolitic sands however, being subjected to high and low velocity wave and tidal currents, can be formed into a variety of structures, in the same way as sandbanks in clastic environments. Common bedding structures are plane bedding, cross-bedding and cross-lamination of both symmetrical and asymmetrical type. Bioturbation is fairly uncommon in this high energy environment. By contrast however, lagoonal sediments are usually so highly bioturbated by organisms that all original structures are removed, though sometimes lamination and the cross-lamination associated with wave and current ripples are found. In lagoons bordering arid coastlines, the strong evaporation can produce saline conditions on the shoreward side of the lagoon. This discourages organisms, so lamination structures are more likely to be preserved.

Fauna and flora

The fauna and flora that live in these tropical seas have already been mentioned in some detail. Organisms preserved in the reef and reef talus are often broken and abraded. Although the carbonate sands that form barriers may be composed of skeletal particles, these high-energy areas provide fairly poor conditions either for life or for preservation, so well-preserved organisms are rarely found. It is in the lagoonal sediments that the best conditions for living and preservation occur, so here well-preserved organisms are common.

Geometry of the sediment body

A classification of reefs and reef geometries was first attempted by Charles Darwin following his voyage on the *Beagle*. He recognised three main reef types: **fringing reefs**, where the reef develops outward from the shore; **barrier reefs**, which may be up to several kilometres off shore and which therefore enclose a lagoon; and **atolls**, the roughly

Figure 2.18
Darwin's theory of reef development on a subsiding volcanic island.
If subsidence were faster than upward coral growth, what would be the result?

1. Fringing reef   2. Barrier reef and lagoon   3. Atoll and lagoon

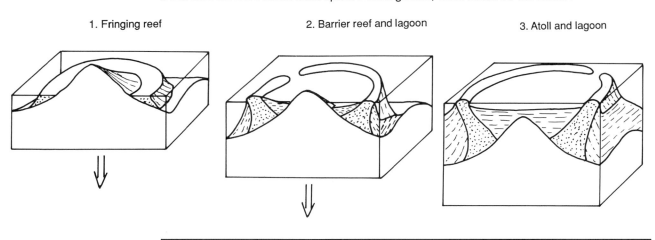

circular reefs enclosing lagoons that are found in oceanic areas. In 1837 Darwin went on to offer an explanation for these reef types. His explanation is shown in Figure 2.18. Darwin realised that corals can only grow on a hard basement, and that the coasts of oceanic islands provided ideal coral-growth points. Thus he postulated that fringing reefs formed around oceanic islands, which were then subjected to subsidence. As subsidence of an island continued, the reef built out and the island became smaller until finally just the reef was left as an atoll. This hypothesis could be tested by drilling a borehole through an atoll, but the technology to do this was not available in Darwin's day. If a borehole showed that deeper coral samples became progressively older until a basement of volcanic rocks was encountered, this would be very good evidence for Darwin's hypothesis. Many attempts at drilling such a hole have been made over the years. They showed that the age of the coral did increase with depth. But it was not until 1952 that a borehole actually reached a basement, which proved to be volcanic. Thus Darwin's linking of fringing reefs to barrier reefs to atolls seems to be a good explanation of reef formation in oceanic areas. We now think that the subsidence of volcanic islands is associated with plate tectonic movement. As the plate is carried away from a mid-oceanic ridge area, it cools and subsides, carrying down any volcanic areas that have developed. It is now thought that changes in sea level also play an important part: rising sea levels, for example, can cause islands to 'sink beneath the waves'.

A similar theory linking subsidence to changes in sea level is advanced to account for the formation of the barrier reefs associated with continental margins, such as the Great Barrier Reef of Australia.

To the three reef types identified by Darwin (fringing, barrier and atolls) we should add **patch reefs**, irregular-shaped reefs which form in lagoonal and shelf areas. It is now thought that the surfaces of reefs and lagoonal areas were changed and sculptured when falls in sea levels during the Quarternary caused their higher levels to be exposed above the water. Then chemical weathering produced **karst** topography (an irregular surface produced by faster rates of chemical weathering in some places than in others) on the upper surfaces of the reefs. When sea levels rose again, the high points that had been exposed remained as reefs and grew upwards, whereas the lower submerged areas became filled with sediment. This process is shown in Figure 2.19, and it might explain the origin of many of the patch reefs in lagoonal and shelf areas.

Reef or barrier geometry greatly controls the shapes of the whole carbonate depositional environments. On broad shelves widespread blankets of carbonate sediment form, whereas on barrier and fringing reefs the belts of carbonate sedimentation become

Figure 2.19
The evolution of reefs due to changes in sea level and attack by weathering. (After Purdy, 1974; in Reading, 1978.)
Why does the inner part of the reef form a more irregular surface than the outer face?

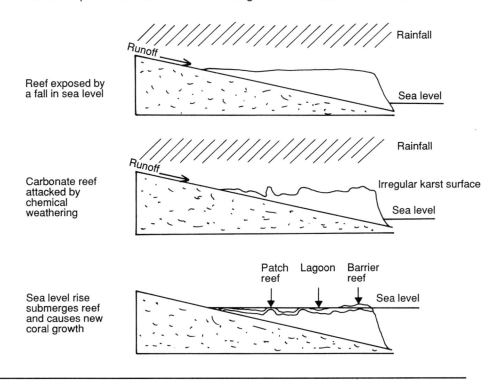

progressively narrower. Within lagoonal areas, layered sediments are disturbed in places by patch reef development.

Resultant sequence
In carbonate areas of net deposition, the shelf will be subsiding or the sea level rising. In both cases the effect produced is the same, as is shown in Figure 2.20. The barrier grows outwards over its own talus and upwards as subsidence progresses. The lagoonal sediments grow outward and upward over the old reef. Eventually a vertical sequence is formed consisting of open sea shelf facies covered by reef talus (**fore-reef**) facies,

Figure 2.20
The sequence produced by the upward and outward building up of a reef.
How would a similar build-up of an oolitic sand bank environment differ from this?

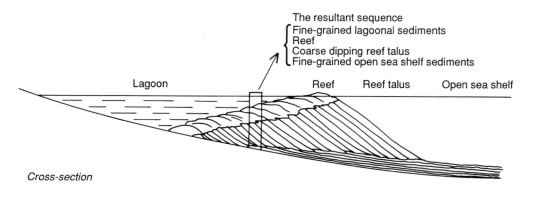

followed by reef, then **back-reef** lagoonal facies. In this way the lagoonal area becomes broader and broader – unless coastal sediments build out over the inner margins of the lagoon.

Examples in the British Isles

Reef sequences of fore-reef talus, reef and back-reef lagoonal sediments are well preserved in the middle Devonian of south Devon and in the Carboniferous limestone of Derbyshire. During lower Carboniferous times the Derbyshire area consisted of a raised platform within a deeper sea. Reefs developed right around the margin of the raised platform, creating a large lagoon in the centre (see Figure 2.21). Outside the reefs, the reef talus grades into the deeper-water, finer-grained sediments. In places, the reefs have become exhumed (i.e. exposed after being buried) by erosion, and form ridge barriers as they once must have done in the Carboniferous seas.

Figure 2.21
A simplified palaeogeographical map of the Derbyshire area during the lower Carboniferous. (From Ford and McKerrow; in Kennett and Ross, 1983b.)
How would the environment and the sediments deposited in Carboniferous times have changed along a west–east line drawn across the area? Illustrate your answer with a cross-sectional diagram.

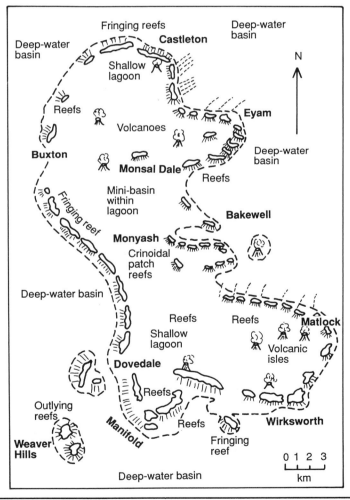

In the middle Silurian, a broad shelf area extended across the Shropshire region and, during the deposition of the Wenlock Limestone, many small patch reefs developed on the sea floor. In parts of the Wenlock Limestone, whole sea-floor communities are beautifully preserved as **life assemblages** (i.e. groups of fossil organisms preserved in their original living positions) under the quiet conditions that must have prevailed at that time.

Bahama-like conditions developed during the middle Jurassic in southern England, particularly in the area from Bath to the Cotswolds, where rippled and cross-bedded oolitic sands were deposited. Finer lagoonal sediments were laid down behind the oolitic sand barriers.

Arid Shorelines and Evaporites

Evaporites are minerals that crystallise out from saline water during evaporation. The major source of saline water for the production of evaporites is the sea. Normal marine water contains a variety of dissolved salts which produce a salinity of 35 parts per thousand (35‰) i.e. 3.5 per cent. The main ions dissolved in sea water are shown in Figure 2.22. The sea water is not saturated in these ions so that they are not normally precipitated. An exception to this is the removal of calcium ions (Ca^{2+}) and hydrogen carbonate ions (HCO_3^-) from sea water by organisms that precipitate calcium carbonate ($CaCO_3$). This form of biogenic deposition of calcium carbonate, as the shells and other skeletal debris of dead organisms, has been covered in the previous section (see page 57).

Figure 2.22
The major ions in sea water.
Weight percentages are percentages of total dissolved material. The salinity (proportion of dissolved salts) of normal sea water is 35 parts per thousand. What is the content, in parts per thousand, of each of the ions in the table in normal sea water?

Positive Ions		Weight %	Negative ions		Weight %
Na^+	Sodium	30.6	Cl^-	Chloride	55.1
Mg^{2+}	Magnesium	3.7	SO_4^{2-}	Sulphate	7.7
Ca^{2+}	Calcium	1.2	HCO_3^-	Hydrogen carbonate	0.4
K^+	Potassium	1.1	Br^-	Bromide	0.2

As sea water evaporates, eventually the brine produced becomes first saturated, then supersaturated, at which point crystals of salt begin to form. The 'salt' is in fact a variety of different minerals. These crystallise in a sequence: the brine, for example, becomes supersaturated with respect to calcium sulphate and precipitates gypsum before it becomes supersaturated with sodium chloride, precipitating halite. The major minerals deposited by the evaporation of sea water are shown in Figure 2.23.

All these minerals are found in the geological record, but they are found in two different types of association. One group comprises thick halite deposits with some gypsum. The other is composed mainly of layered anhydrite ($CaSO_4$) in carbonate sediments. Before 1960 geologists had faced a great problem in trying to understand both these types of deposit, as nowhere on Earth could comparable deposits be found (and therefore studied) which were actually in the process of being formed. It was thought that none existed. However, in the early 1960s a party of geologists from Imperial College, London, was making a study of the low-lying Trucial Coast of the Persian Gulf. Although they were not studying evaporite deposition, they were very surprised to discover that anhydrite was crystallising within the sediments. This was the first known example of modern anhydrite formation. Since then the coastal **sabkhas** of the Persian Gulf have been studied in detail, so the processes of formation of layered sabkha deposits are now much better understood.

Figure 2.23
Major minerals deposited by the evaporation of sea water.
Why should the bittern salts include a variety of minerals?

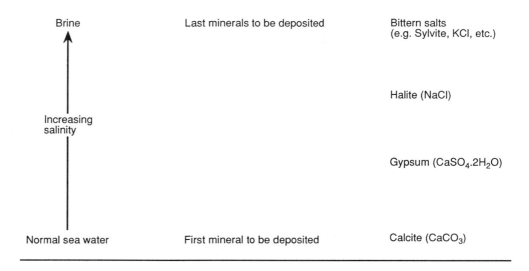

However, large bodies of halite are not forming on Earth today – as far as we know – so we cannot use the present to understand the past in the case of the thick halite deposits in the same way as we have been able to for sabkha deposits. Nevertheless, reasonable explanations of the formation of these 'saline giants' have been put forward. The formation of saline giants and of sabkha deposits will be dealt with separately below, since they are produced by rather different processes.

'Sabkha' Evaporite Deposits

The Arabian name of sabkha has now been given to the type of evaporite deposition that takes place on very low-lying coastal areas in arid regions around the world. These shores have a very gentle slope, so during exceptional tides the whole coastline is under water. Thus, in effect, they are the tidal flats of arid areas.

These areas are extremely flat, hot and inhospitable and would not normally be visited by people from one year end to the next. In these burning conditions very strong evaporation occurs, so the sea water that approaches the coast already has increased salinity, and much carbonate is produced by organisms in the shallow waters off shore. In the tidal zone, large mats of algae develop which bind together the carbonate sands and muds. It is in the area above normal tides that the evaporites form, as is shown in Figure 2.24. The evaporation of groundwater from the supratidal area (the area above normal tides) draws the sea water from the tidal area into the sediments. This water has already lost much of its carbonate so, as evaporation of this groundwater continues, the first mineral to crystallise within the sediments is gypsum ($CaSO_4 \, 2H_2O$). Later on, as more water is evaporated, anhydrite ($CaSO_4$, i.e. calcium sulphate with no water) forms instead, and the gypsum may recrystallise to anhydrite as well. The anhydrite first forms as nodules, forcing the sediments already present apart. Eventually the nodules grow together so that continued growth causes layers of anhydrite to form into wildly contorted shapes, as shown in Figure 2.25. These contorted shapes illustrate the power of crystallisation of the anhydrite. Different forms of anhydrite eventually develop within the sediment, ranging in shape from nodules, through nodules that have grown together trapping thin films of sediment between them (chicken-wire texture), through flat or convoluted layers, to continuous masses of anhydrite (cottage cheese texture).

The groundwaters hardly ever become concentrated enough in sodium and chloride ions to crystallise halite (NaCl), so halite rarely forms in these environments. It

Figure 2.24
Sabkha evaporite deposition by the evaporation of saline groundwater.
Why do sabkhas only develop on the margins of quiet seas in arid conditions?

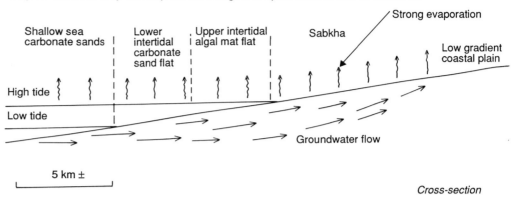

Cross-section

Figure 2.25
Part of a core of sabkha sediment showing the contorted structures formed by the growth of anhydrite.
How could alternating layers of carbonate and anhydrite have been formed?

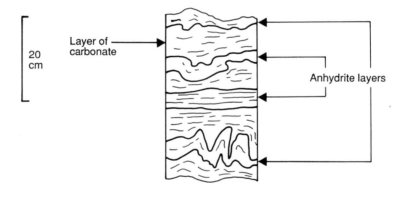

crystallises only when exceptionally high tides cover the sabkha areas, filling any small depressions. Under these circumstances total evaporation of the water causes the deposition of halite.

A very good example of an ancient anhydrite sequence of this type is to be found in the upper Jurassic of Dorset. Here, complete sabkha cycles are preserved, from lagoonal sediments at the base, up through algal mat facies, to the sabkha facies of nodular anhydrite on the top. These cycles illustrate how the horizontal sabkha environments have become preserved as a vertical resultant sequence by the building up and out of the sabkha sediments.

'Saline Giant' Evaporite Deposits

If a volume of normal sea water is evaporated to dryness in the lab, first small quantities of calcite and dolomite are precipitated (less than 1 per cent), followed by a small amount of gypsum (3 per cent), then a large quantity of halite (78 per cent), and finally the **bittern salts**, including sylvite (KC1), are laid down as the last liquid is evaporated off. If you do this experiment yourself using a wok (a basin-shaped Chinese frying pan) you will see that circular salt deposits of smaller and smaller diameters are produced, as shown in Figure 2.26.

Figure 2.26
The evaporation of sea water in a wok, showing diagramatically the development of rings of evaporite mineral deposits. (The layer of calcite and dolomite is thinner than can be shown in the diagram.)
How would the result be likely to change if the sea water were evaporated to half its volume before being used to fill the wok?

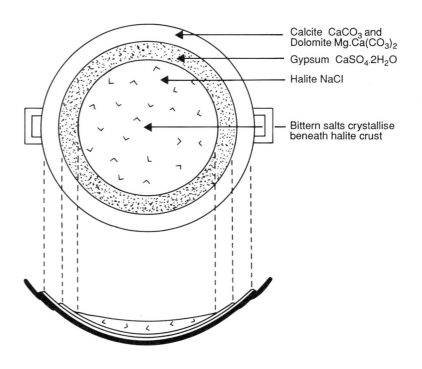

If the percentage of halite crystallised by the evaporation of sea water is compared with the percentage of halite in ancient saline giant deposits (see Figure 2.27), at first sight they seem to be very similar (78 per cent halite in sea water compared with 73 per cent halite in saline giants). However, if the comparison between the salts deposited by normal evaporated sea water and the saline giant deposits is made in more detail, two important problems emerge. The first is that of explaining why preserved deposits should contain more carbonate and gypsum but less bittern salts than the normal sea water. The second problem seems to be a more major one. A 1-kilometre high column of normal sea water, if evaporated to dryness, would produce only a 17-metre thickness of salts. Thus, to produce the 490 metres of evaporite salts preserved in the Permian of parts of Europe, a 29-kilometre high column of sea water would have to be evaporated. This compares with the greatest oceanic depths today of 11 kilometres. As it is unlikely that oceans ever were as deep as 29 kilometres, so it is necessary to find a mechanism other than the simple evaporation of a body of sea water to explain the formation of the saline giants.

The hypothesis put forward to deal with these problems is the barred basin model. The basin is an inlet of the sea with a restricted entrance, as shown in Figure 2.28. In arid conditions the water evaporates from the basin, causing a lowering of the surface, so more water is drawn through the narrow channel at the entrance. In this way the water supply is regularly replenished, and large volumes of evaporite could be built up over time. The extra carbonate and gypsum and the lack of bittern salts in normal sea water can also be explained using this model. As the water evaporates, the salt content of the water increases and the water becomes more dense. First carbonate, then gypsum, then halite crystallise out. Meanwhile, the dense water has sunk to the bottom of the basin and this dense pool of brine, containing dissolved bittern salts in particular, builds up over time. Eventually the brine pool will spill over the edge of the basin out into the open sea, carrying the dissolved bittern salts away.

Figure 2.27
The percentages of evaporite minerals produced by the evaporation of normal sea water compared with the percentages of evaporite minerals found in a number of saline giant deposits averaged together.
Why, in the wok evaporation experiment, is the layer of calcite and dolomite produced so much thinner than the layer of gypsum?

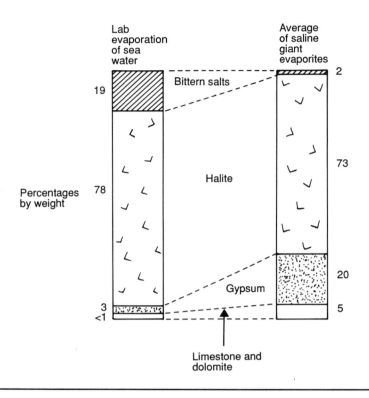

Figure 2.28
The barred basin model for the formation of the saline giant type of evaporite deposits.
Why does most of the evaporite crystallisation occur near the inner margin of the basin?

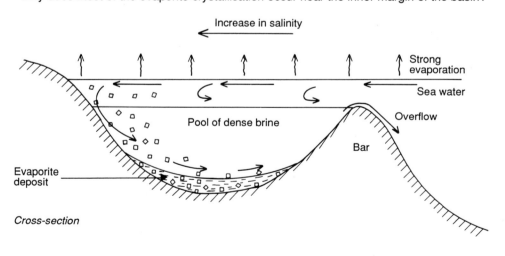

Some of the saline giants do contain sequences of evaporites like those formed in the wok experiment. Carbonates are followed by gypsum or anhydrite and then thick halite, capped by bittern salts, each type of salt occupying a progressively smaller area. This shows that the basin that deposited the evaporites acted like a wok: the basin became filled, then no more water came into the basin as evaporation occurred, so the water occupied a smaller and smaller area as the salts deposited. However, since several evaporite cycles of this type are recorded from some deposits, water must have flooded into the basin periodically and the evaporation cycle was thus repeated. Incomplete cycles were formed when water flooded the basin before complete evaporation had taken place. This basin model is therefore a modification of the barred basin model described above: sea level is below the level of the bar most of the time, but inundations over the bar do occur periodically. During these floodings, bittern salts may be washed out.

These models can only be hypotheses since, as the saline giant type of large-scale evaporite deposition is not happening today, the process cannot be observed. However, deposition of the wok type, producing alternating layers of gypsum and halite, does occur today in shallow depressions called **salinas** on the margins of the northern end of the Gulf of California in Mexico. Another modern example of evaporite deposition similar to the saline giant type is to be found in the Gulf of Kara Bogaz on the eastern side of the Caspian Sea. In this barred basin, strong evaporation is causing halite to be precipitated, together with some unusual magnesium sulphate evaporite minerals. Given these modern comparisons, the hypothetical models seem reasonable as explanations of the saline giant formation process.

Saline giant forming conditions have occurred in Britain in the past, the best known being the upper Permian Zechstein deposits in north-east England. The Zechstein was a large saline sea that extended from the North Sea area over much of northern Europe as far as Poland. The western margin of this sea overlapped the coast of north-east England depositing more than 450 metres of evaporites in places. Five major evaporite cycles are recognised, some with the complete sequence of carbonates, through anhydrite to thick halite capped by bittern salt deposits. A number of minor cycles, such as halite–anhydrite alternations are superimposed on the major cycles. The presence of these evaporite sequences leads geologists to the interpretation of an ancient barred basin with periodic inundations from the sea.

Another example of saline giant formation occurred during the arid conditions of the upper Triassic in the Cheshire Basin area, continuing to the Isle of Man. There, salts with a total thickness of about 600 metres were deposited. These are largely thick halite deposits although gypsum layers do also occur. Again, the barred basin model is used to explain these deposits. The Cheshire Basin area has been an important economic source of salt (halite) for many years.

Recognising Shoreline Sediments

As has been shown, a wide variety of shoreline depositional environments exists today, ranging from very high to very low energy, with biological and chemical processes playing important roles at times. There is therefore a broad variation of deposits being produced now, and a similar variety was formed in the geological past too. Certain clues are available for recognising the types of sediments formed under shoreline conditions. For example, the majority of shoreline processes produce well-sorted sediments because of the great energy available in wave and tidal currents and the fact that deposition by settling produces only fine-grained sediments. Coarser sediments also tend to be reasonably well rounded.

Symmetrical wave ripples form only in shoreline environments, since shallow waters on the margins of large bodies of water are necessary for their formation by waves. Interbedded rippled sands and muds are particularly characteristic of tidal deposits.

Coastal deposits in temperate regions are usually characterised by abundant to fairly abundant life, indicated by the number of body and trace fossils present. Some trace fossils, such as those shown in Figure 2.29, are found only in ancient sediments deposited in the tidal zone and so are very good evidence for a shoreline environment.

Figure 2.29
Trace fossils found associated with sediments deposited in the tidal zone (i.e. from the normal high water zone to shallow tidal waters just offshore). (Based on Collinson and Thompson, 1982.)
The *Diplocratarian* burrows illustrated have been given the name *Diplocratarian yoyo* because they show how the burrowing organism moved its burrow up and down. Which of the *Diplocratarian* burrows shown demonstrates an upward movement, which a downward movement, and which both? Why should the organism need to move its burrow up and down?

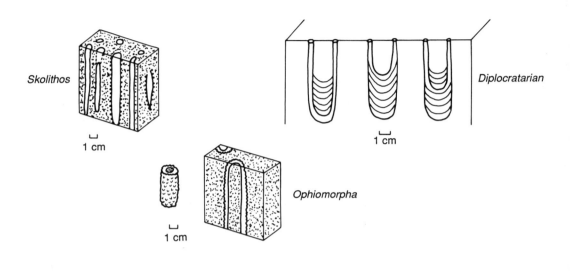

Extensive coarse- to medium-grained carbonate deposits develop only in warm coastal areas; extensive evaporite deposits are likely to have formed in arid areas adjacent to oceans or seas.

As these examples show, there are a number of pieces of evidence which can be used to identify shoreline deposits. Often, however, one piece of evidence alone is insufficient, in which case a number of 'clues' must be looked for to enable accurate identifications of shoreline sedimentary bodies to be made.

Economic Aspects

Coastal Defences

The longshore drift process (described on page 40) carries sediment along a coast; this can cause several major problems. Where sediment is swept away from the bases of cliffs which are formed of easily-eroded rock, the protection of the beach is removed, allowing the waves to attack the cliffs directly. This can cause enormous problems of cliff collapse and subsidence on the cliff top. Roads, railways, houses, etc. situated on the cliff top can slide down, either gently or, sometimes, catastrophically. In Britain this is a particular problem for the Jurassic and Cretaceous clay cliffs of Dorset and the Isle of Wight, the Tertiary clay cliffs of Hampshire and Sussex, and the Pleistocene till cliffs of East Anglia and much of the coast of eastern England.

Longshore drift can also be a problem for seaside resorts in cases where the sandy beaches are swept away leaving nowhere for children to dig with buckets and spades and spoiling the image of the resorts for tourists. Increased erosion of promenades can also be caused, necessitating expensive maintenance and repair.

In the places where the sediment that is moved along the coast is finally deposited, there can be problems too. Spits of sand or shingle that build out into estuaries can create a hazard or an inconvenience to shipping such that expensive dredging of channels has to be carried out.

In the long term, in all these cases, the sea will win. However, in the short term a number of measures can be taken to protect a coastline, particularly where buildings, roads and tourist images are at risk. One of the simplest and cheapest of these measures is to build series of **groynes** or barriers across the beach at right angles to the shore, as is shown in Figure 2.30. The sediment builds up on the up-current side of the groynes, slowing down its movement along the coast and producing a stepped beach pattern.

Figure 2.30
Groynes built to slow down longshore drift along a beach.
What were the directions of the waves and the drift movement that have produced this pattern?

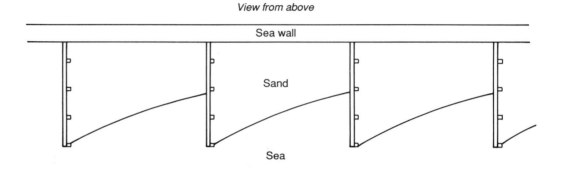

Where this is only partly successful coastal engineers have to take stronger measures, such as building sea walls or placing large rectangular wire baskets (called gabions) filled with stones at the feet of vulnerable cliffs. A number of other measures to improve the drainage and increase the stability of clay cliffs may also be taken.

Coal Swamps and Coal Measures

Some of the thickest and most widespread coal deposits on Earth developed in the delta top environments found over much of northern Europe in the upper Carboniferous. The sequences thus formed are called the **Coal Measures**. Despite their name, the Coal Measures consist mostly of sedimentary rocks other than coal. They are mainly sandstones and shales with, at intervals, relatively thin coal seams, ranging from thin coaly streaks to thicknesses of about 2 metres. The Coal Measures are largely a series of cyclic sediments called **cyclothems**, as can be seen in Figure 2.31. In this figure there are, above the lowest coal seam, three coarsening-upward deltaic sequences, each capped by a coal seam formed in a delta top swamp environment. The top cyclothem is a more complete cyclothem than the others: it begins with a marine band, which is followed by a lagoonal sequence containing fresh water bivalve fossils (known as **non-marine lamellibranchs**). Both of these were formed before the delta sequence capped by a coal seam developed.

The interpretation of this sequence is that in the overall delta top environment, small-scale deltas built out into interdistributary bays. The cycles were caused either by avulsion diverting a distributary into the bay environment, or by subsidence of the land, or by sea level changes. Whatever caused the cycles, the result, when a complete cycle developed, was of shallow marine conditions in the bay, followed by fresh water lagoonal conditions as the fresh water from the distributary flooded the area, followed by the small delta building into the bay at the end of the distributary. As the top of the

Figure 2.31
A typical Carboniferous Coal Measure sequence shown in a simplified form.
What factors could cause 'incomplete' cyclothems to develop?

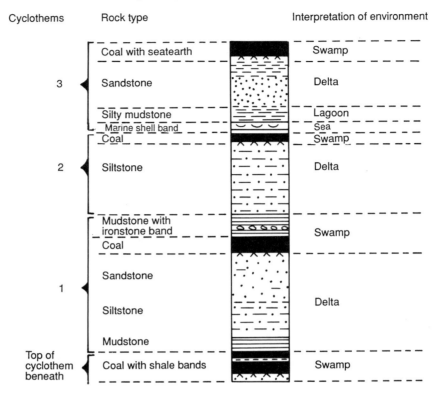

delta came to the surface of the water, it was colonised by dense vegetation. This led to the formation of a soil. As the vegetation continued growing, organic debris from dead vegetation built up, gradually forming a thick accumulation of peat. The peat eventually became altered to coal (the way in which peat changes to coal through diagenesis is described at the end of Chapter 5 of *Sedimentology Book 1*) and the compacted soil beneath the coal became a **seatearth**. Repetition of this cycle, or part of it, has produced the many coal seams with seatearths found in the Coal Measures.

Wherever Carboniferous Coal Measure sequences are preserved in Britain, coalfields – past or present – are found. Even tiny outcrops often still contain the evidence of opencast workings from the nineteenth century. The largest working coalfields in Britain today are the York, Notts and Derby coalfield and the Northumberland and Durham coalfield, but fields in Scotland, north-west England, the Midlands and South Wales have also been very important. These areas have been, and still are, mined by both deep mining and opencast methods.

In the past the seatearths of the Coal Measures have also been of economic importance. Sometimes in the acid swamp soils of the delta top environment, iron-rich layers developed which eventually became ironstone bands, as shown in Figure 2.31. These ironstones are of too poor quality to be worked now, but they were the main source of iron in Britain at the beginning of the industrial revolution, because they were very conveniently found with the coal that was necessary to smelt the ore to form iron. This is why many of the heavy iron- and steel-making industries in Britain began on or next to the coalfields. Some are still found there today.

Other seatearths were leached in the tropical delta top conditions to form very pure silica soils. These are now called **fireclays** if of clay-grade, and **gannisters** if of sand-grade material. Being very pure silica, they have been widely used to make furnace linings that were not affected by the high temperatures produced by the furnaces.

Whilst it was the Carboniferous period that saw the greatest development of coal swamps in Britain (and, indeed, the world), coals have also formed at other times. In Yorkshire for example there are thin coals that formed on the tops of deltaic sequences in the middle Jurassic.

Hydrocarbons in Deltas

A significant part of the world's oil and gas comes from deltaic deposits such as those of the Mississippi and Niger deltas. This is because the delta deposits contain hydrocarbon sources, in the form of coal (producing gas), and deeper water organic accumulations (producing oil). They contain abundant reservoir rocks with high porosities in the form of distributary channel fills and delta front sand complexes and there are many cap rocks in the form of interdistributary bay muds, etc. The shapes of the sand bodies themselves often provide the necessary traps: for example, a sandy channel sequence preserved within and capped by fine-grained delta plain deposits makes a fine hydrocarbon trap.

Limestone

Limestone is the most commonly quarried of all rocks in the British Isles and it has a tremendous variety of uses. In the past it has been very important in building. Its use as dimension stone, i.e. load-bearing stone, can be seen in many cathedrals and public buildings throughout Britain, as well as in towns and villages situated in limestone areas, such as the Cotswolds. In areas like the Cotswolds where it is too expensive nowadays to use cut natural stone to make new buildings, but where planning departments require that the new buildings blend in with the old ones, quarried stone is crushed and re-made into rectangular building blocks of the same colour as the original. Today, load-bearing structures are largely made of concrete and steel rather than of dimension stone, but limestone can still be widely seen in its use as a decorative or facing stone on shops, buildings and mantlepieces. Fossiliferous limestone is particularly popular for this use.

Large quantities of limestone are quarried for **aggregate**. The aggregate, i.e. crushed stone, is used to bulk out concrete, and as the foundations of roads and runways.

Much limestone, particularly chalk, is quarried for cement manufacture. To make cement, the limestone is heated with clay until some of the carbon dioxide is expelled and calcium silicates form. The resultant stoney material is powdered and sold. Most cement is either used, with aggregates of various types, to make concrete or is mixed with sand to make mortar for building brick walls.

Limestone is also used in steel making, to remove the impurities as slag. It has wide uses in the chemical and glass-making industries and has probably been used as a filler for the paper you are reading from now. It is used as a filler to bulk out a number of other products too and is also important for gas purification.

Lime, made by heating limestone to change it to calcium oxide, has been essential to the farming of heavy acid soils in the past and its use continues today. In coastal areas of acid soils, ruined lime kilns can be found in many inlets and estuaries. These were where in the past limestone, brought ashore in flat-bottomed boats, was roasted and then spread on the nearby fields. Today the lime is delivered by lorries instead.

These are just some of the many industrial uses of lime and limestone today.

Oolitic Ironstone Deposits

The Coal Measure ironstone bands were the focus of the first development of the iron and steel industry in Britain. The second development was on the outcrop of lower Jurassic iron ores found in Northamptonshire, Lincolnshire and Yorkshire. There the ironstones are oolitic and are composed of the minerals chamosite (hydrous iron silicate), siderite (iron carbonate) and limonite (hydrous iron oxide).

These ironstones pose an interpretation problem for the geologist, since oolitic ironstones are not known to be forming on Earth today. Normally these iron minerals only accumulate under reducing (i.e. non-oxygenated) conditions, whereas ooids form only in the well-oxygenated waters of shallow active seas. One possible solution to this problem is centred on the observation that chamosite formation, in particular, is associated with faecal pellets. The faecal pellets suggest a high content of organic material in the sediment. This may remove enough oxygen for the iron minerals to form despite the fact that the environment is active enough for ooids to form. Further changes may occur during diagenesis.

The Jurassic ironstones are not widely worked today because their iron content only ranges up to about 30 per cent, whereas vast reserves of ironstone in other parts of the world have ores containing more than 65 per cent iron. Thus the focus of the British iron and steel industry has now moved to the coast where shipments of iron ore from overseas can be received. Modern steel plants are, however, still largely situated on coastal coalfields to keep fuel transportation costs to a minimum.

Evaporites as Economic Minerals

The majority of salt (halite, $NaCl$) extraction in Britain comes from the Cheshire Basin area, where it has been exploited for many years. In previous centuries the practice was to pump salt-saturated groundwaters out from above fairly shallow salt deposits. The brines obtained were then evaporated to crystallise the salt. This was the cheapest way of recovering the salt but it did have disastrous environmental consequences at times. As the salt was removed from shallow depths, the caverns formed by its removal sometimes collapsed, causing whole houses to disappear into holes in the ground.

Today, salt is recovered from deep deposits so that any subsidence that does result is only minor by the time it reaches the surface. However, as groundwater flow is slow at depth, extra water has to be provided to speed up the process. In fact, warm waters are pumped down to dissolve the salt, and the brine is then pumped out for the salt to be recovered by evaporation.

In addition to this method, there is also one working salt mine in Britain, where the salt is removed by normal mining techniques. The rather impure salt so recovered is ideal for melting snow and ice on roads in winter.

You may be familiar with one of the major uses of salt, that of food seasoning and preservation. But you may not have realised that the main use of salt is in the chemical industry. Much of our salt production goes to make sodium carbonate (soda ash) which is used in the manufacture of glass, soap, washing soda and various sodium chemicals. Sodium hydroxide (caustic soda) is produced by the electrolysis of salt and is used in the manufacture of soap and artificial fibres; in the extraction of aluminium; to digest the wood in pulp and paper manufacture and in refining petroleum. Chlorine, which is also made from salt, is widely used in bleaching and in the manufacture of hydrochloric acid, and has many other applications besides, including the chlorination of swimming pools. These are just a few of the chemical processes in which salt plays a key role.

Gypsum (hydrated calcium sulphate) is another evaporite mineral that is important economically. Most British gypsum extraction comes from the Permian Zechstein deposits in Cleveland. Some gypsum is used as a fertiliser, some to slow down the setting of cement, but the vast majority of gypsum is converted to plaster of Paris (so named because of the important gypsum deposits near Paris). This is done by heating the gypsum to drive off most of the water. When plaster of Paris is mixed with water, it sets to a fairly hard mass, as you will have seen if you have ever broken a limb and been plastered.

Plaster of Paris is used extensively in the building industry for plastering walls and for making plasterboard. Much is also used in the pottery industry to make the moulds for casting various pieces of pottery such as cups and jugs.

The Zechstein bittern salts are also worked in north-east England for their content of potassium salts such as sylvite (KCl). Although they are highly soluble, they are extracted by mining rather than by brine pumping. Potassium salts are converted to potash (K_2O), a vital fertiliser. Lack of potash during the First World War is supposed to be the main reason why some vegetables were of such poor quality. Potassium fertilisers therefore, are very important for agriculture.

Evaporite and Hydrocarbon Reservoirs

A significant number of the hydrocarbon reservoirs of the North Sea and elsewhere in the world have been produced by evaporites which act in two ways. Since evaporites have lower densities than the rocks which overlie them and since they are able to flow under pressure, 'bubbles' of evaporite can flow upwards, first doming upwards, then breaking through, the overlying rocks, as is shown in Figure 2.32. The evaporites rise

Figure 2.32
The development of salt diapirs, shown in cross-section.
Where are the oil and gas traps likely to be located? Show them on a copy of this diagram.

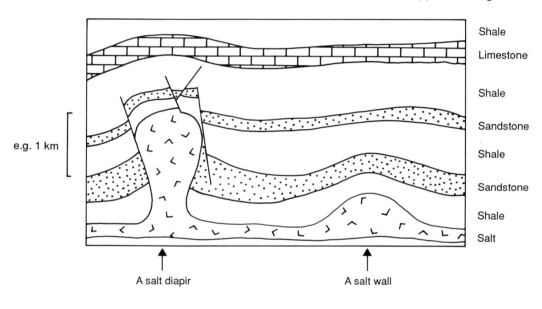

e.g. 1 km

Shale
Limestone
Shale
Sandstone
Shale
Sandstone
Shale
Salt

A salt diapir   A salt wall

until they reach equilibrium with the pressure of the overlying rocks. The rising evaporite 'bubbles' are called **salt domes** or **salt diapirs** and they move upwards until they reach equilibrium. Often the formation of one diapir triggers the creation of another, so large areas of evaporites develop diapiric structures, as has happened beneath the North Sea and on the coast of Texas, USA. In both of these cases hydrocarbon traps have been formed. Diapiric structures also form beautifully in the ornamental table lamps you may have seen that contain two non-mixing fluids so chosen that, when the lower fluid becomes warmed by the lamp it becomes less dense and rises in bubbles into the upper fluid.

Evaporites are also important in oil- and gasfields as cap rocks. Not only are they impermeable but, if faulting occurs, the evaporites can flow, thus 'healing' the fractures such that the hydrocarbons are retained in the traps. Evaporite seals are important in several of the North Sea gas reservoirs and in the Rainbow Reef oilfields in Alberta, Canada.

Practical Investigation and Fieldwork

Carry out the investigations described below in order to gain a better insight into the processes described in this chapter and the effects they produce.

Please note: a wave tank suitable for use in Investigations 1–5 has been described by Whitfield, 1979. Tanks can also be bought from school suppliers of geological equipment.

1. How do waves form in water?
Fill a plastic or glass tank or bowl (or a specially designed wave tank) with water. Make waves in the water in as many different ways as you can think of. Each of the ways of making waves you have discovered is active in the natural world too. Explain how.

2. How do waves form ripples in sand?
Place two or three dessertspoonfuls of washed sand in the bottom of a rectangular glass or plastic tank (or a wave tank). Add a few centimetres of water. Spread the sand to make a fairly even layer on the floor of the tank. Either rock the tank gently, by regularly raising and lowering one end, or by rocking the tank on a wooden rod or by rolling the tank backwards and forwards on two wooden rods or, if you are using a wave tank, start the paddle. You decide on the best method and the best speed of movement. Watch the bed of sand carefully for the development of ripples. When ripples have formed, stop rocking the tank or stop the paddle, but allow the water to 'rock on'. Watch how the movement of crests and troughs of waves relates to the movement of the sediment on the sides of a ripple. Show your findings in a diagram. What is the shape of the ripples formed in plan view and in cross-section?

Repeat the experiment with poorly-sorted sediment and with a mixture of sand and higher density corundum powder to test the sorting power of waves.

3. How does the wave power necessary to form ripples change with grain size?
You need a wave tank about a metre long with either a hand-operated or motor-driven paddle for this experiment. You also need supplies of sieved sand of various grades. Fill the tank with water up to the level of the paddle. Place a flat bed of medium sand (0.5–0.25mm diameter) on the floor of the wave tank. Set a wave rate of a certain number of paddle movements per minute (a small number to begin with). If no ripples form in the sand, increase the wave rate by a fixed amount. Repeat this procedure until ripples are formed. Record the wave rate at which ripples first form. Repeat the experiment for sand of coarse sand size (1–0.5mm diameter). Plot your results on a graph of wave power, i.e. wave rate, (side of graph) against sediment size (base of graph). Repeat the experiment for the other grades of sediment you have available and plot these results on the graph. Join the points plotted with a smooth line. The graph you produce may be similar to the graph of Figure 2.5 (see page 43) which was produced by a similar set of experiments. What do you predict would happen if coarser grades or finer grades of sediment than you had available were used?

4. How does wave power change up a sloping bed?
Set up the wave tank with a slope towards the paddle so that the floor of the tank emerges above the water about two-thirds of the way along its length. Set a paddle rate to produce waves that move up the sloping bed nearly as far as the top end of the tank. Take single grains of coarse sand and drop them at various places up the sloping bed to find the first position at which this size of grain is moved by the waves. Record this position on the side of the tank using a wax pencil, and on a scale drawing of the side of the tank. Repeat the experiment with grains of different sizes, from very fine sand to granule-grade material and add the results to your diagram. On the basis of these investigations, where would you expect the coarsest material to be concentrated in a beach environment? Where would the finest material be found? Why are waves such good sorters of sediment?

5. How does longshore drift operate?

Set up the wave tank with a shallow dip to one corner near the paddle. Add enough water to make the paddle effective and to form a diagonal 'shoreline' across the upper end of the tank. Start the paddle. If waves reach the top end of the tank, increase the tilt until they don't. Add a few grains of coarse sand to the wave area. Observe how the sand is moved by each successive wave. Show your observations in a diagram. Repeat the experiment with floating particles, such as a few small flakes of cork. Add your new observations to the diagram. Notice what happens to the particles when drift has carried them to the edge of the wave tank.

(Investigations 3, 4 and 5 were first described by King, 1980.)

6. How do deltas develop?

Set up a stream table or tray filled with sand dipping gently towards a sink. Pipe water onto the top end of the tray and allow a pool to build up in the bottom end. Observe the processes that operate as a channel builds a micro-delta out into the pool. Observe the delta top, delta front and pro-delta areas. What triggers the formation of the delta? Where are the highest current velocities? Where does sedimentation occur the fastest? Do the same processes operate on different parts of the delta? Is sedimentation continuous? Does the delta continue to develop or does another delta lobe begin to form? What causes the channel switch?

'Fossilise' the shape of the delta by dropping some sand of a different colour over the top and front of the building delta at intervals. Allow the table to drain overnight and then cut cross-sections of the delta using a ruler. Which beds are thicker: the delta top or the delta front beds? Have pro-delta beds developed? If not, why not? Record your observations.

7. How do beaches and tidal flats work?

Beaches and tidal flats are similar in that they both tend to produce bands of environment parallel to the coast. A number of the processes which are active are similar in both, although others are different. The investigation described here could be carried out for either a beach or a tidal flat, but it is better to do both in order to be able to make comparisons.

Find a suitable beach or tidal flat. Make a line transect across the bands of environment at right angles, i.e. from the sea towards the shore. Make observations at fixed intervals, the intervals measured by pacing. You will need at least six observation stations. At each station record on an observation sheet like the one shown in Figure 2.33, the following, as appropriate:

sediment size and sorting;
sediment composition;
type and trend of sedimentary structures;
number and types of living organisms;
number, type and state of preservation of dead organisms;
percentage cover of vegetation;
number and types of species of vegetation;
number and depth of burrows.

You will have to work out your own methods of making these measurements so that they are comparable from station to station. Then record, for each station, which of the following processes you think are active according to your observations:

wave, current, settling or wind processes;
bioturbation by animals;
binding and baffling by plants.

A combination of these processes may be operating.

Figure 2.33
An observation sheet for recording changes across modern sedimentary environments. (From King, 1984.)
Which observation method is most appropriate for each of the observations – e.g. distance = pacing; sediment size = use sediment size comparator; type of sedimentary structures = in an area of 5 metres around observation station; etc.?

MODERN SEDIMENTARY ENVIRONMENT OBSERVATION SHEET

LOCALITY NAME _____ GRID REFERENCE _____ TRANSECT/GULLY NO. _____

Observations	Observational Method	Stations								
		1	2	3	4	5	6	7	8	9
Distance from base line										
Sediment size										
Sediment sorting										
Sediment composition										
Type of sedimentary structures										
Trend of sedimentary structures										
Number of living organisms										
Types of living organisms										
Number of dead organisms present										
Types of dead organisms										
Preservation of dead organisms										
Percentage cover of vegetation										
Number of types of vegetation										
Types of species of vegetation										
Number of burrows										
Depth of burrows										
Slope										
Carbonate content										
Gully width										
Gully depth										
Processes Active										
Deposition by waves										
Deposition by current										
Deposition by settling										
Deposition by wind										
Bioturbation by animals										
Binding by roots of vegetation										
Baffling by vegetation										

If gullies or channels cross the beach or tidal flat, these are separate and different environments and should be ignored on the first transect, but a second transect following a chosen gully or channel should be made to record its features in the terms listed above.

Plot your results as a series of graphs, from sea to land, showing how the environment and processes change across the transect.

Once you have made all your observations, you can use them to build a hypothetical model of the environment and the sedimentary sequence that is likely to result. The beach or tidal flat must be a depositional area, otherwise it would not be there. If it has net deposition, then it must be building up over time. Build-up over time will cause the sea to be moved back and so the bands of environment will build upwards and outwards, as shown in Figures 2.7 and 2.10 (pages 46 and 50). Thus the vertical sequence eventually produced will be the same as the horizontal sequence you observed on your transect. More seaward processes will have operated at the base of the sequence with more landward processes operating at the top. The change eventually preserved from bottom to top in the preserved sequence will be the same as those you have shown in your graphs, from sea to land. Your hypothetical model of a beach or tidal flat sequence can now be used to find similar ancient sequences, which could then be interpreted in terms of beach or tidal flat processes.

(These investigations were first described by King, 1984. See also Kennett and Ross, 1983b for details of an investigation into the ecology and zonation of organisms in a modern beach environment.)

8. Which types of organisms are bioclastic beach sands made of?

Collect a variety of shells and other organic materials from a beach and/or tidal flat. Sort the materials into species groups. Either weigh each group or measure the sizes of the five largest specimens in each group and calculate the average weight or size. Record your results. Place all the materials into a wide-necked large plastic bottle. Add several pebbles (rounded beach pebbles are best, but any type of pebble-sized rock can be used). Shake the container vigorously for 15 seconds. Empty the container and sort the organisms into species groups again. Reweigh or remeasure the groups and record the results. Replace all the material in the container. Repeat the exercise several times. Plot the results on a graph of shaking time against weight of species group or average size of five largest specimens. When you have completed the investigation, examine the organisms that were the best survivors. What characteristics do they have in common? Can you think why they might have these characteristics? Which characteristics did the non-survivors have in common? Why? Study the bioclastic carbonate sand produced by the investigation using a hand lens. What characteristics of size, shape, angularity/roundedness and sorting do the grains have? What are the likely similarities and differences between the bioclastic sand you produced and the bioclastic sands found on the beaches of tropical islands? What is the preservation potential of a plastic container in a beach environment?

(This investigation was first described by Kennett, 1983.)

9. How do evaporite sequences form?

Carry out the wok experiment, described on page 64, in the lab (or kitchen!). Fill the wok to the brim with sea water, set it over a very low heat and leave it for several hours. Return at intervals to check its progress. For the best results, remove it from the heat when a small amount of brine remains and complete the evaporation over a radiator or in a warm room such as a glasshouse. Why are circles of deposits formed? Can you identify each of the minerals that crystallises? What are the crystal shapes of the minerals formed? In which part of the fluid do each of the types of crystals grow? Where do the bittern salts crystallise? How could the evaporite cyclothem you have produced be repeated? How could the deposition of calcium sulphate salts be caused without the crystallisation of halite in a cyclothem? When you have finished the experiment clean out the wok, or else the salts will take in water from the atmosphere causing fast rusting.

Test Your Understanding

1. Figure 2.34 shows stratigraphic logs which are the resultant sequences of four of the depositional environments described in this chapter, i.e. beach, tidal flat, delta, reef/lagoonal, carbonate bank/lagoonal, sabkha or saline giant. Which sequence was produced by which environment? Explain your reasoning by reference to several of the characteristics of each log.

Figure 2.34
Stratigraphic logs showing simplified resultant sequences from four environments. (The graphic log symbols used are those given in Figure 1.8, page 13.)
Two are recent sequences (based on Evans, 1970; in Selly, 1986), one from the margin of the Dutch Wadden Sea and one from the coast of Abu Dhabi in the Persian Gulf. Of the remaining two ancient sequences, one is from the middle Carboniferous of Yorkshire and the other from the upper Jurassic of Dorset. Which is which? Explain your reasoning.

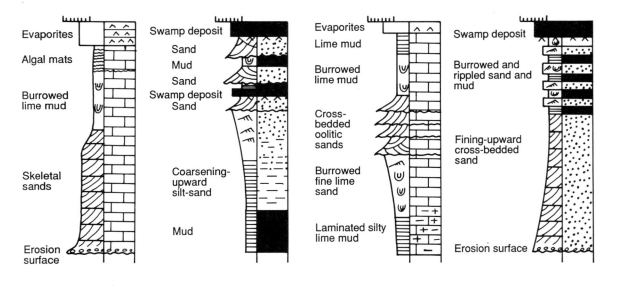

2. Why do many British beach sands show weight-reductions when treated with dilute hydrochloric acid? How would similar treatment affect tropical beach sands?

3. When oil geologists find shoe string sands that contain hydrocarbons, it is extremely important to distinguish beach sands from delta channel sands. Beach sands will be parallel to the palaeo-shoreline, but delta channels will be at right angles to it. Thus in the case of beach sands, prospecting should continue parallel to the palaeo-shore, whereas for channel sands it should be at right angles to it. Describe the features that would enable a geologist to distinguish a delta channel deposit (which has great similarities to meandering stream channel deposits) from a beach deposit.

4. The varied coastline of the British Isles contains many estuaries, great and small. However, estuaries are very short-lived in terms of geological time. Why?

5. Sedimentary structures formed in sands in tidal flats and estuaries can be used to work out the directions of the currents that formed them. Which structures would be suitable for this? Why do some structures indicate currents in one direction while others indicate currents from the opposite direction?

6. Ribbon lakes have developed in many of the U-shaped glacial valleys of Scotland, the Lake District and Wales. Streams that flow into the sides of these lakes usually deposit sediments that form an alluvial fan which becomes a delta beneath the water. What shapes would you expect these deltas to form in plan view? Explain your answer.

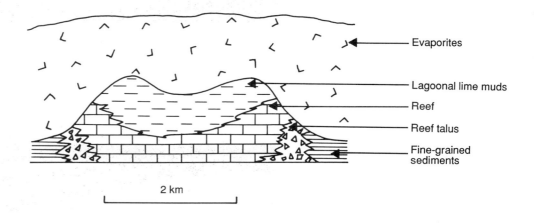

7. The Rainbow Reef complex in Alberta, Canada is an important oilfield. Figure 2.35 shows a cross-section of one of the reefs. What forms the cap rock in this sequence and why? Which of the facies within the reef sequence are likely to be most important as reservoir rocks (assuming that there were few changes in porosity and permeability during diagensis)? Explain your reasoning.

Figure 2.35
Cross-section of one of the reefs in the Devonian Rainbow Reef complex in Alberta, Canada. (From Baars et al., 1970; in Selly, 1976.)
What was the environment like in this area during Devonian times?

— Evaporites
— Lagoonal lime muds
— Reef
— Reef talus
— Fine-grained sediments

2 km

8. What features would enable you to distinguish a fossilised reef talus, as found in the lower Carboniferous rocks of Castleton in Derbyshire, from a fossilised Pleistocene scree deposit as found at Ecton Hill in Staffordshire? When you have answered this question, consider how the situation you have described is complicated by the fact that the Ecton Hill scree fragments are actually of lower Carboniferous limestone.

9. Jurassic oolitic limestone is the building stone that gives Cotswold villages their character. Many of the building blocks show cross-bedding. How did the cross-bedded oolites form?

10. An area of Tatton Park in Cheshire suddenly began subsiding about a hundred years ago. The subsidence occurred over a roughly circular area about 0.5 kilometre in diameter and the tension produced at the surface resulted in a number of normal faults and small scale rift valleys. Eventually the area subsided beneath the water table and a lake formed. Since it was shown that the activities of chemical companies in the Cheshire area had not resulted in the subsidence, what natural phenomenon might have been the cause? Explain your reasoning.

11. The Cheshire salt mines have been considered as repositories for the disposal of high-level nuclear waste. What features make salt mines suitable for radioactive waste disposal and what features might cause problems? What particular drawbacks might be related to the salt mines in Cheshire?

12. In modern coal-mines the coal is cut by a cutting machine with rotating blades that moves backwards and forwards along the coal face cutting off a slice of coal each time. The broken coal falls on to a conveyor belt and is carried away. Such mining methods are badly affected by washouts and seam splitting, as shown in Figure 2.36. Why is this? How could washouts form in the coal swamp environment? How could the conditions that produce seam splitting develop in a delta top environment?

Figure 2.36
Coal mining problems: A – washout; B – seam splitting of the type developed in the South Staffordshire Coalfield.
Taking into consideration the delta top environment in which coal is formed, what other problems for mining can you think of that could be caused by features of the depositional environment?

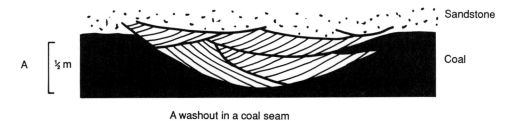

A   ½ m

Sandstone

Coal

A washout in a coal seam

Cross-sections

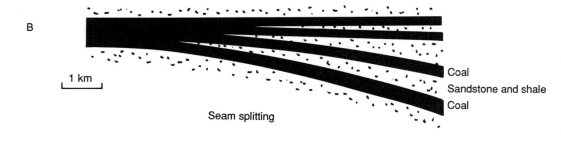

B

1 km

Coal
Sandstone and shale
Coal

Seam splitting

3. DEPOSITION OFFSHORE

Offshore environments can be classified as shown in Figure 3.1. **Epicontinental seas** are the shallow sea areas that develop on the continent but are connected to the oceans, examples being the Baltic Sea and the North Sea. Their shorelines may or may not be strongly tidal. On the margin of the continent, beyond the **tidal** or **littoral** zone, is the shallow water zone of the **continental shelf**. The surface of the continental shelf is irregular but it becomes generally deeper outwards from the coast as far as the **shelf break**. The depth of the shelf break is variable but averages about 200 metres. The irregular surface of the shelf has a mean depth of about 130 metres. Beyond the shelf break the true oceanic area begins above the **continental slope**. While the continental slope can be fairly steep in places, it generally has a gentle slope (averaging 4°) downwards to the **continental rise** which is linked, by an even more gentle slope, to the **abyssal plains** of the ocean floor. Abyssal plains are 4–5 kilometres deep and are

Figure 3.1
A diagrammatic cross-section to show the major areas of sedimentation in seas and oceans. Where else could littoral zones develop on the diagram? How would sea level rises and falls, as occurred during the Pleistocene glaciations, affect the environments shown?

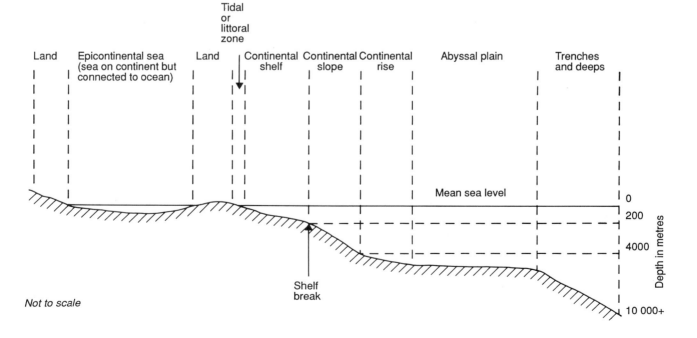

very broad and generally flat, but with ocean deeps and rises developed in places. Islands, seamounts and guyots (flat-topped seamounts) rise from the abyssal plains in parts of the oceans. The deepest areas are the **trenches** which, in places, are more than 10 kilometres deep.

The 200 metres average depth of the shelf break is also important as it is the maximum wave base i.e. the maximum depth that is affected by waves during storms. Thus shelf environments are affected by waves whereas oceanic areas are not. Also, tidal effects can be strong in shelf areas, whereas they are negligible in deeper regions.

The **photic zone** or zone of sunlight penetration also has a maximum depth of about 200 metres. However, this is only in ideal conditions of very clear waters. Normally, in murky oceanic and shelf waters it is far less deep. Nevertheless, sunlight can penetrate to the floors of shelf areas, whereas oceanic depths are totally dark. This contrast is important as the abundance and variety of life in any one environment is closely linked with the amount of sunlight available.

In summary, shelf seas and epicontinental seas are well lit and subject to wave and tidal forces; whilst waves and sunlight affect the surface zones of oceans, none of these factors affect areas beyond the shelf break, in the depths of the oceans.

Shallow Seas

Conditions of initiation

The conditions of initiation of a shallow sea environment are, simply, depth and sea. The depths vary from about 10 to 200 metres and the conditions are normal marine, i.e. with no great influxes of fresh water and no strong evaporation causing increases in salinity. These conditions are found in two types of area: epicontinental seas and shelf seas. However, a better subdivision of shallow sea environments is based upon the main processes that are dominant in them. These are either tidal- or wave-dominated processes. Tide or wave domination can affect both shelf and epicontinental seas. For example, the epicontinental North Sea and the shelf seas to the west of Britain are dominated mainly by tides, whereas the shelves of the east coast of the USA and the partly enclosed Bering Sea off Alaska are dominated mainly by waves.

All modern shallow sea environments have been complicated by the fact that sea level was a good deal lower during the Pleistocene ice ages when much water was locked up as ice on the continents. At this time, most of the floors of today's shallow seas were above water level and subjected to fluvial or glacial conditions. When sea level rose in the Holocene transgression between 17,000 and 7,500 years ago, these land areas, covered in sediments, were flooded. In places where seas are quiet today the sediments remain as **relict** (left behind) features on the sea floor. On active floors the sediments have provided sources of sediment and have modified modern sea floor processes. It is often very difficult to determine whether sediment bodies found on sea floors today have been produced by modern processes, are relict but have been modified by modern processes or are simply the remains of ancient processes.

Transportation and deposition of sediments

In shallow seas, transportation and deposition are caused mainly either by tides or by waves. These will be dealt with separately.

Tides are caused by the pull of the moon and the sun, as described on page 47. Since the water must move to produce the tidal bulge that affects all marine areas of the Earth twice a day, strong tidal currents can be generated. This is particularly so where coasts tend to funnel the tidal effect, either by converging coastlines or by a steady shallowing of the sea floor. In addition, it often happens that one state of the tide has stronger currents than the other. Sediment will be moved by both flood and ebb tidal currents, but if flood currents are stronger, there will be net transportation of sediment in the flood direction; if ebb currents are stronger, overall transportation will be in the ebb direction. Thus tidal currents can be powerful movers of sediment in shallow sea areas such as those off the British coast, as shown in Figure 3.2.

Where there is net transportation of sediment by tidal currents away from an area of the sea floor (i.e. an area of bedload parting) as seen off the south coast of England near the Isle of Wight, this is likely to be an area of erosion and the sea floor will be covered by lag gravels left behind by the removal of sands and muds. Where net transportation is towards an area, bedload convergence occurs and sediments tend to build up. This fairly simple picture is more complex in reality, as seen by a comparison of Figures 3.2 and 3.3. Where deposition takes place at areas of bedload convergence, fields of sand waves can often develop.

Figure 3.2
Dominant sand transport paths by tidal currents on the north-west European continental shelf. (After Stride, 1965 and Kenyon and Stride, 1970; in Leeder, 1982.)
Why do tides that both ebb and flow often result in overall sediment transport in only *one* of these directions?

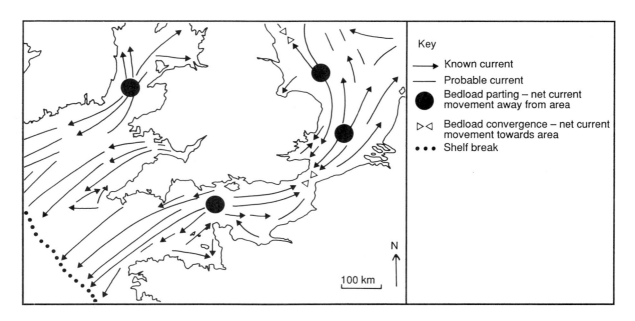

Wave-dominated shallow seas usually have low tidal ranges and weak tidal currents. Normal wave action, as described on page 38, causes bidirectional movement of sediment at depths down to about 200 metres during storms. Normal wave action can also produce wave-driven currents that are strong during storms. Another feature that is particularly important in coastal areas is storm surge, when wind effects can cause high tides to be much higher than usual. Storms are particularly important in wave-dominated seas since greater depths are only affected during storms and storm-produced features at shallower depths may well survive the gentle reworking of more normal conditions. Long parallel sand ridges often form in this type of environment.

The sediments in wave-dominated seas tend to become finer and finer offshore as depth increases until mud becomes the main deposit. Tidal seas also contain low energy areas with floors of mud (see Figure 3.3). In normal conditions these mud floors are good areas for life and so bioturbation is common and preservation potential for organisms is high. However, where the oxygen supply is restricted, so are the numbers and variety of organisms and bioturbation is greatly reduced.

Figure 3.3
The distribution of sediment types on part of the north-west European continental shelf. (From Stride, 1963; in Selley, 1976.)
How can the mud deposits of the western Irish Sea and the gravel deposits in the English Channel, south of the Isle of Wight, be explained?

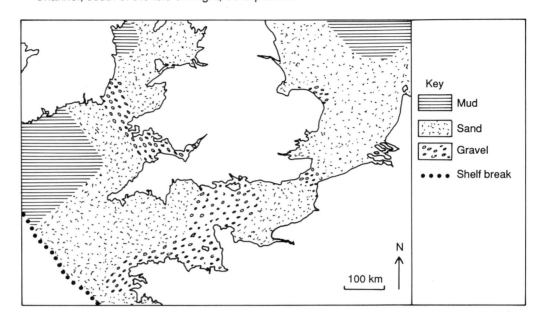

Key
- Mud
- Sand
- Gravel
- Shelf break

100 km

N

Sediment types

Shallow sea sediments can be carbonate-rich if developing off areas where carbonate is forming today. In areas of clastic input the mobile sediments are sand and mud, as is shown in Figure 3.3. In areas of erosion, either bedrock or gravel is found. The gravel is what remains of the relict sediments after erosion of the finer materials. Shelf sediments generally become finer towards offshore areas, although this picture is complicated in strongly tidal areas. Since the sediments are moved frequently, they are usually well sorted and rounded and the sands are mature. The muds are often bioturbated and pelleted.

Certain **authigenic** minerals (i.e. minerals that grow within the sediment as it is being deposited) form in shallow sea environments. **Glauconite** is an important example of such minerals. Glauconite is a green hydrous iron and potassium silicate which is easily recognised because of its colour. It is important because it forms only in shallow seas and thus indicates, for example, that the glauconite-rich Cretaceous greensands found in southern England must have been formed in a shallow sea environment. Glauconite is also valuable because it contains potassium, which can be radiometrically dated. Thus absolute ages can be obtained for the time of the sediment formation. Such absolute ages of sediment formation are usually very difficult to obtain. Other authigenic minerals found in shallow sea sediments include phosphates, and iron minerals such as chamosite and siderite.

Sedimentary structures

In tidally-dominated environments, current-formed sedimentary structures develop, from small to large scale. The large-scale structures called **sand waves** and **sand ribbons** are, it seems, only found in tidal shallow seas. Sand waves are large transverse dune-like bodies up to about 15 metres high. Sand ribbons are long strips of sand up to 15 kilometres long and less than 1 metre high. It is thought that sand waves form rather like transverse dunes do in desert regions (see page 22) while sand ribbons have similarities to seif dunes, being formed by current vortices (see page 23). **Tidal sand ridges** are much larger features, being up to 40 metres high, 2 kilometres wide and 60 kilometres long, and they are particularly well developed in the southern North Sea. It is thought that these may be relict features that formed before the rise in sea level and have since been modified by modern tidal conditions.

A variety of other current-formed structures develop in the sands of tidally-dominated environments, such as ripples, subaqueous dunes and plane beds. A particularly common feature in tidal sands is **herringbone cross-bedding** (see Figure 3.4). This is formed when one dune is moved in one direction during the flood tide, then another dune is moved in the opposite direction during the ebb. The result is a series of cross-bed sets dipping in opposite directions, one above the other. Tide-dominated areas are also subjected to wave action, so symmetrical ripples are common too. In areas of mud deposition, any lamination is often destroyed by bioturbation.

Figure 3.4
Herringbone cross-bedding, as formed by tidal currents moving in different directions during ebb and flow.
In this diagram, does the dominant tidal direction appear to have been towards the left or towards the right?

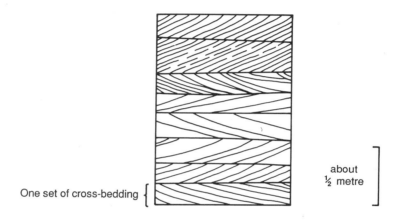

One set of cross-bedding {

about ½ metre

In wave-dominated areas similar small-scale sedimentary structures such as ripples, the cross-bedding associated with dunes, plane beds, lamination and bioturbation are found. The common larger scale structures are **sand ridges**. These are bars of sand up to 10 metres and tens of kilometres long which, it is thought, form during storms but are maintained during normal conditions.

Fauna and flora
Fauna and flora are active under these shallow sea conditions, as is shown by the variety of tracks, trails and burrows formed in the sediment. Some traces, such as those shown in Figure 3.5, are particularly characteristic of ancient shallow sea environments. Shell banks and layers can be formed in both sands and muds, and are often composed of organisms swept out from nearer the coast during storms.

Geometry of the sediment body
The geometry of shallow sea deposits is of irregular sheets covering broad areas of the sea floor. The irregularities are caused either by the development of large-scale sedimentary structures, or by other undulations of the top or bottom surfaces of the deposit.

Resultant sequence
The resultant sequences of shallow sea deposits, if they are sands, are often called **sheet sands** or **blanket sands**, reflecting the fact that they are extensive (possibly several hundreds of square kilometres in area) and relatively thin (tens to hundreds of metres thick). The sequences do not usually change in character from bottom to top in a regular

Figure 3.5
Trace fossils typical of shallow sea environments. (Based on Thompson, 1986 and Collinson and Thompson, 1982.)
Cruziana and the associated traces are thought to have been made by trilobites (an extinct marine organism with many limbs which it used for both walking and swimming). How might each of the traces shown in the *Cruziana* diagram have been made by a trilobite?

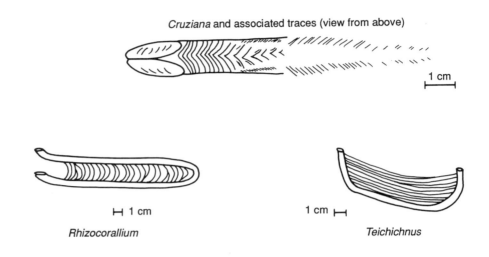

Cruziana and associated traces (view from above)

1 cm

H 1 cm

Rhizocorallium

1 cm H

Teichichnus

way, but their features remain fairly constant. Sands are mature and contain glauconite and other authigenic minerals. They are often extensively cross bedded and cross-bed dip directions indicate deposition by bidirectional currents. Cross-lamination produced by current and wave ripples is also common.

Examples in the British Isles

Some good examples of ancient shallow marine sheet sands can be found in Britain. They include the late Precambrian Jura quartzite found on the islands of Jura and Islay in western Scotland. This changes away from the palaeo-shoreline from cross-bedded sandstones to cross-laminated sandstones and mudstones. The change is thought to be due to a reduction in energy across a tidally-dominated shelf sea. Sand waves are also preserved in the sequence.

Other examples include the Cretaceous Lower and Upper Greensands which are both rich in glauconite and contain structures such as sand waves and herringbone cross bedding sets, as well as ripples and shallow sea faunas. The Greensand outcrop runs across the country, from Lincolnshire to Dorset, as well as surrounding the Weald in Kent and Sussex. The Lower and Upper Greensand outcrops sandwich the Gault clay which is a mud deposit that formed in the lower energy, deeper water conditions which prevailed between the two episodes of sheet sand development.

The Jurassic sequence in Britain contains many muds and some sands of shallow sea origin. The Jurassic outcrop which stretches from Yorkshire in a broad curving belt to the south coast of England has at its base the lower Jurassic Lias. The Liassic sequence is mainly mud with thin limestone bands that formed when the supply of mud was reduced. The sequence contains abundant ammonites and bivalves, and in places large marine reptiles such as ichthyosaurs are preserved. Bioturbation and wave ripples are locally abundant. However, the lower Jurassic sea floor undulated and on the swells, sandy facies and carbonate sequences developed. Similar conditions to those of the lower Jurassic also developed in the upper Jurassic when the Oxford Clay and the Kimmeridge Clay were laid down. Some of the quiet shallow seas that developed at these times had poor oxygen supply, so they contain **restricted faunas** i.e. the preserved remains of the few species that were able to adapt to the oxygen-poor environment. Where faunas are restricted, the numbers of fossils is also reduced and burrowing is far less common. At times the environments were so euxinic (oxygen poor) that bituminous oil-rich muds accumulated, later to become oil shales.

Shallow sea muds and sands also had widespread development in south-east England during the Tertiary when changes in sea level caused sequences of deeper muds followed by shallower sands and then by estuarine and fluvial facies to be deposited in a series of cycles.

Finally, a British example of long-lasting shelf sedimentation that cannot be omitted is the shelf sequence of muds, sands and limestones that formed in South Wales and the Welsh borderland from Cambrian, through Ordovician, to Silurian times.

Ocean Margins

The ocean margins comprise the continental slope and the continental rise, and the deep ocean floor adjacent to these. These areas are shown in a seismic profile in Figure 3.6, but note that this type of seismic plot produces great vertical exaggeration, so that continental slope which appears almost vertical in the profile only has a dip of about 4° in reality.

Figure 3.6
A seismic profile across the margin of the Atlantic Ocean off New York City, showing continental slope, rise and abyssal plain. (After Emery et al., 1970; in Reineck and Singh, 1973.)
Note that the scale of half travel time in seconds that is used greatly exaggerates the vertical scale. What is the explanation for the irregularities shown in the continental rise sediments?

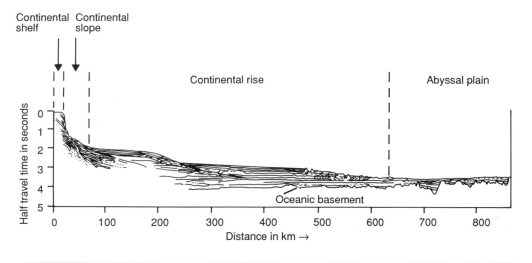

The continental slope is not smooth but is indented by **submarine canyons** like the one shown in Figure 3.7 in map and cross-section. These may have steep-sided walls and extend for tens of kilometres down the slope. The origin of these undersea valleys is not certain, but they probably developed when sea level was much lower, during the ice ages. Beyond the mouths of submarine canyons, **submarine fans** may develop, forming part of the continental rise.

Sediment is transported across the continental shelf by wave and tidal action. The sediments may accumulate as thick deposits on the continental slope itself but much of the material is frequently fed directly to submarine canyons, so these are major channels of sediment movement. The movement may be continuous, but often sediment on both the slope and in the submarine canyons builds up. Movement of these piles of unstable waterlogged sediment is triggered by an unusual event, such as an

Figure 3.7
Map and cross-profiles of The Gully, a submarine canyon in the continental slope off the east coast of Nova Scotia, Canada. (After Marlowe, 1965; in Keen, 1968.)
What is the gradient of the canyon floor? The profiles have been drawn with a vertical exaggeration of five times. What is the actual gradient of the steepest slope shown?

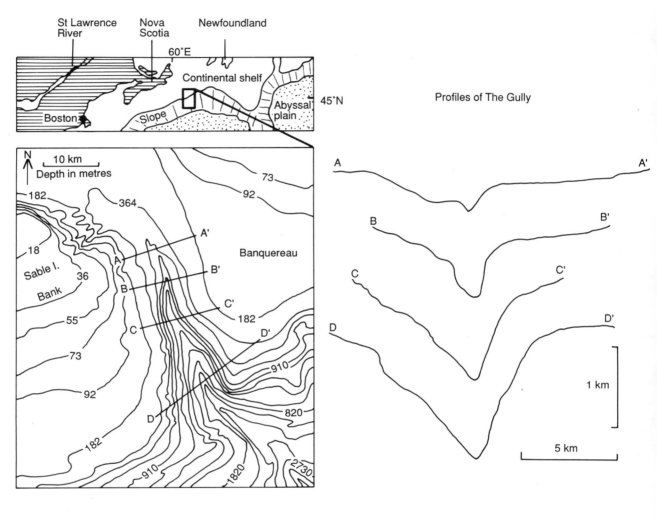

earthquake or storm. This causes the sediment to slide then slump, often developing into a debris flow or a turbidity current which can move downslope at high velocity (these mass gravity transportation processes are described in more detail in *Sedimentology Book 1*, pages 24–31). Thus seismic profiling of the sediments on continental slopes and rises often shows evidence of sliding and slumping. In submarine canyons, fast flows of sediment can move downslope to the mouth of the canyon and out over the submarine fan. These sediment movements are shown in diagrammatic form in Figure 3.8.

The submarine fans that develop at the mouths of submarine canyons are similar in many ways to alluvial fans, as described on page 4. Both are fan-shaped with the point of the fan at the mouth of a channel in a slope. They both slope gently outwards and have a series of distributary channels developed on their upper surfaces, which often have levées developed on their margins, as shown in Figure 3.9. Fan lobes build out in the same way as they do for deltas, until eventually avulsion occurs, the old lobe is abandoned and a new lobe begins to develop. As submarine fans are areas of great deposition, like deltas they tend to be built outwards and upwards over their early deposits, producing coarsening-upward sequences like the one shown in Figure 3.10.

Figure 3.8
Continental slope topography and processes shown in diagrammatic form.
What could be the major processes that transport sand *along* the coast to the heads of submarine canyons? Why should the mud be carried out to sea instead?

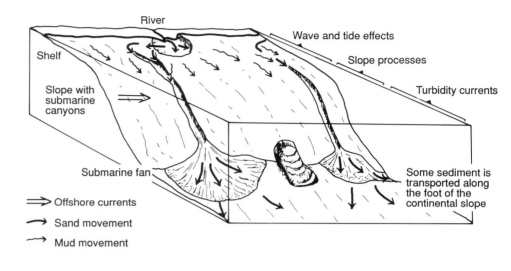

Figure 3.9
A model of a submarine fan.
The fan is built up by near-source turbidite deposits. (After Normark, 1970; in Reading, 1978.)
How do the levées on the margins of the central valley form?

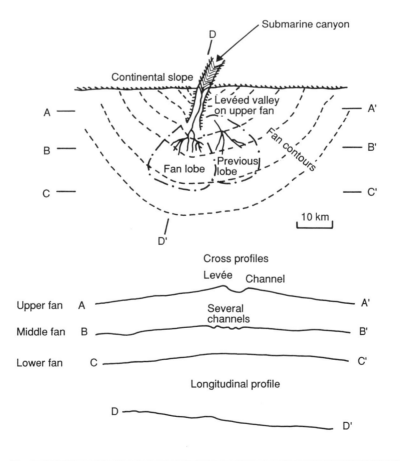

Figure 3.10
A diagrammatic stratigraphic log of the resultant sequence likely to be produced by a submarine fan deposit. (Refer to the key given in Figure 1.8 on page 13.)
Individual fan lobes coarsen upwards, individual channel fill deposits fine upwards, but there is an overall coarsening upwards. (Based on Walker and Mutti, 1973; in Leeder, 1982.) How are individual beds in the outer fan likely to change in grain size upwards?

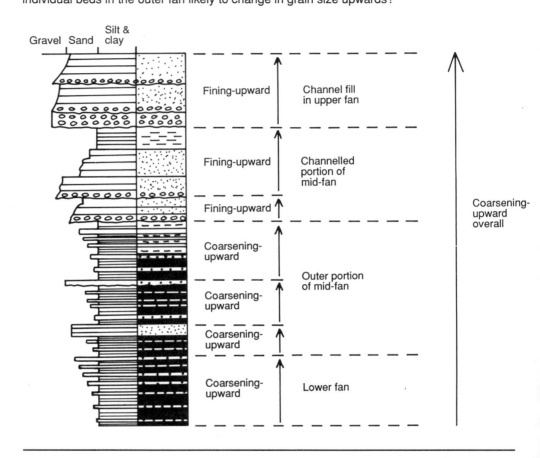

The importance of **offshore currents** in these continental margin areas (as shown in Figure 3.8) has only been recognised in the past few years. They are currents which are part of the main oceanic circulation. Before they were discovered, the ocean margin floors were thought to be very quiet areas that were engulfed from time to time by turbidity current flows. Now the offshore currents which flow *along* the continental slopes (unlike many other currents that flow *down* slopes) have been shown to be quite strong enough to erode, transport and deposit the fine-grained sediments found in those regions, producing lamination and sometimes rippling. Since they follow the contours of the continental slope they are often called **contour currents** and their deposits are called **contourites**.

Despite the importance of contourites in some places, the major agents of deposition (or rather, of re-deposition) in most oceanic margin areas are turbidity currents, which will now be considered in more detail.

Conditions of initiation
Turbidity currents are flows of sediment-laden water beneath a larger standing body of water. The sediment suspended in the water makes it more dense. This denser water remains at the bottom and is able to flow fast downslope. Turbidity currents can flow wherever sediment-laden water is introduced to a standing water body. These conditions of initiation can occur in bodies of water of various sizes, from puddles to ponds and lakes, but their greatest importance by far, both in terms of scale and the volume of sediment transported, is in ocean margin regions, including trenches.

Transportation and deposition of sediments

Turbidity currents were first recognised as important agents of sedimentation in the 1950s and it was at this time that the results of the Grand Banks earthquake of 1929 were reinterpreted in terms of turbidity currents (see *Sedimentology Book 1*, pages 29–30). Until this time the thick deposits of widespread alternating beds of sandstone and shale, called **flysch**, were not understood in terms of their environment of deposition. Now, most geologists consider that they were deposited by ancient turbidity currents and they are therefore called **turbidites**.

These currents are triggered on the continental slope and, having begun as slides or slumps, soon become debris flows. (The formation of these is described in detail in *Sedimentology Book 1*, page 29). The debris flows may not develop beyond this and many examples of massive, poorly-sorted, deep sea debris flows are known, some of which can extend for hundreds of kilometres. Usually, however, the flows take in enough water to become density or turbidity currents. These are fast-flowing and their movement downslope gives them enough impetus to carry them for hundreds, perhaps thousands, of kilometres across the ocean floors.

Sediment types

The sediments involved in turbidites are of sand, silt and mud grade. Most turbidites are poorly sorted and, since turbidite sandstones usually contain more than 15 per cent mud matrix, they are **greywackes**. Many turbidite sandstones are also immature because, although they may have been carried for great distances, there has been no attrition or breaking down of the buoyed up particles. Thus many turbidite greywackes contain more than 25 per cent feldspar and so are also **arkoses**. They may contain other materials that have been swept down from the continental shelf, so that plant fragments are common and shallow water organisms are also preserved at times. Even sands containing glauconite have been found in turbidites.

Sedimentary structures

Turbidites are recognised by their regular sand-shale alternations and by their wide lateral extent and regularity, but sedimentary structures also play a key role. The typical turbidite sequence was first described by Bouma in 1962 and is now called the **Bouma sequence** (see Figure 3.11). The formation process is thought to be as follows. The ocean floor is covered by layers of **pelagic** mud (see page 97) which have settled from

---

Figure 3.11
The Bouma sequence – the graded bed deposited by a slowing turbidity current.
How does the sequence of sedimentary structures formed by a slowing turbidity current compare with the sequence produced by slowing water currents in lab experiments, as shown in Figure 1.3 (page 9)?

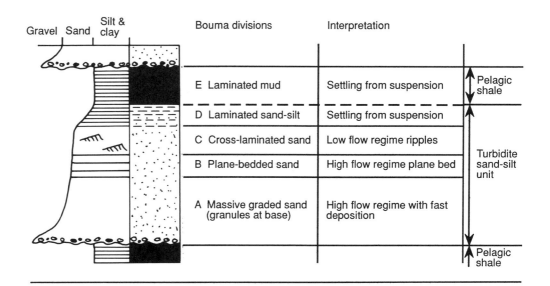

suspension. As the head of the fast-flowing turbidity current passes over the mud, this mud is eroded. Often a small eddy or vortex will form in the water as it flows over the mud and a series of such vortices produces spoon-shape depressions in the mud which widen down-current, called **flute marks** (shown in Figure 3.12). **Tool marks** are produced by 'tools', i.e. bits of debris, marking the mud as they are moved along. They

Figure 3.12
Flute casts on the base (sole) of sandstone beds.
In which directions must the currents have been flowing to produce the flutes in each of the cases shown?

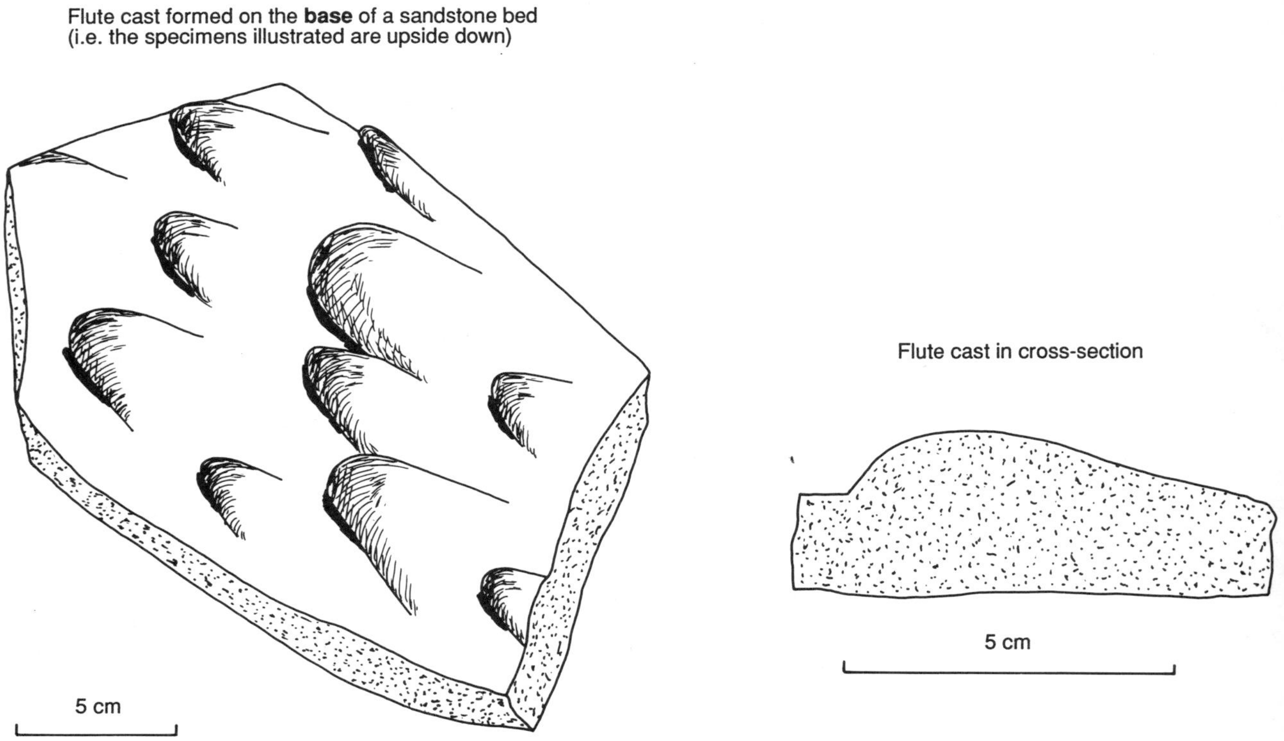

Flute cast formed on the **base** of a sandstone bed
(i.e. the specimens illustrated are upside down)

Flute cast in cross-section

5 cm

5 cm

include **groove marks** which are made by material being dragged along the mud, and **prod** and **bounce marks**, formed by debris such as bits of shell etc. prodding or bouncing along the mud in passing. These become preserved because sand is then deposited over these depressions by the turbidity current, thus making casts (shown in Figure 3.13). **Flute casts** and **groove, prod** and **bounce casts** together are called **sole structures,** as they are all found on the sole or base of the sand bed. Other sole structures are produced when the tracks and trails of organisms become filled with turbidite sand and are preserved as casts.

When sole structures become preserved in sandstone which is later exposed in a cliff section, the mud or shale beneath the sandstone often becomes eroded away. The sole structures are then exposed and are best seen by looking upwards towards the base of the sandstone beds. Safety helmets are very necessary when doing this. Flute casts are very useful for giving palaeocurrent directions, as they open down-current. Groove casts can give palaeocurrent trends only.

After the high-velocity turbulent turbidite head has passed by, deposition begins as the current slows down and the Bouma sediment sequence begins (as shown in Figure 3.11). First a massive (structureless) sand is deposited under high flow regime conditions which cause no layering. As the depositing current is slowing down, grain

Figure 3.13
The formation of sole marks as casts in sandstone.
It is possible to work out the trend of flow of the current which produced these marks, but not its direction. Why is this?

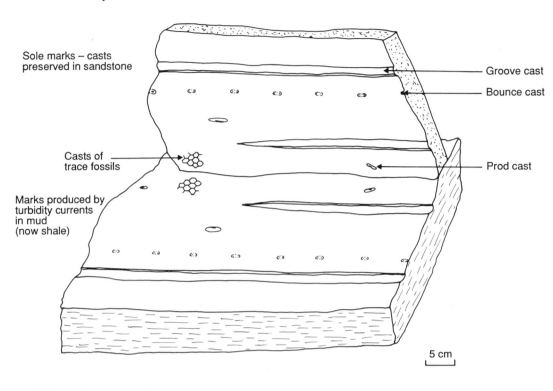

Sole marks – casts preserved in sandstone

Groove cast

Bounce cast

Casts of trace fossils

Prod cast

Marks produced by turbidity currents in mud (now shale)

5 cm

size decreases upwards, i.e. grading occurs. This is Bouma's A division. The slowing current then deposits sand under high flow conditions that produce plane bedding (B division), after which low flow regime conditions prevail, depositing rippled sand which is seen as cross-lamination in cross-section (C division). This is followed by laminated sands and silts (D division) which are the last deposit of the current as it disappears across the ocean bed. Finally, the original quiet conditions of settling pelagic mud take over to produce the laminated mud of the E division.

This whole sequence is a single bed, it is deposited by one sedimentary event. As it becomes finer from bottom to top, it is called a **graded bed**. Such a fining-upward *bed* should not be confused with fining-upward *sequences*, which are produced by a series of sedimentary episodes. The vast majority of sandstones with graded bedding in the geological record were produced by turbidity currents. Thus, when coupled with sole marks, which are also produced almost exclusively by turbidity currents, they are very good indicators of an ocean margin, turbidity current dominated environment. Graded beds and sole structures are also very useful as **way-up criteria**. Sole marks are found only on the *bottoms* of sandstone beds. Inversely graded beds (i.e. ones that coarsen upwards) are very uncommon. Thus, if you find a sequence that contains sole structures on the *tops* of sandstone beds, and graded bedding that coarsens *upwards*, the sequence must be inverted, i.e. it must have been turned upside-down by tectonic forces.

After the deposition of a turbidite, the sand at the base of the sequence, being more dense than the waterlogged mud beneath, may collapse down into it forming small folds called **convolute bedding**. The sand lumps are called **lode casts** and the mud which is squirted up between the lodes produces **flame structures**, as shown in Figure 3.14. These post-depositional sole structures are also useful as way-up criteria – since sediment can't collapse upwards!

Figure 3.14
Convolute bedding caused by the collapse of sand layers into the 'sloppy' water-filled mud layers beneath.
Why, in this example, did the thicker layers of sand form convolute bedding, while the thinner sand layers did not?

Before collapse  After collapse to form convolute bedding

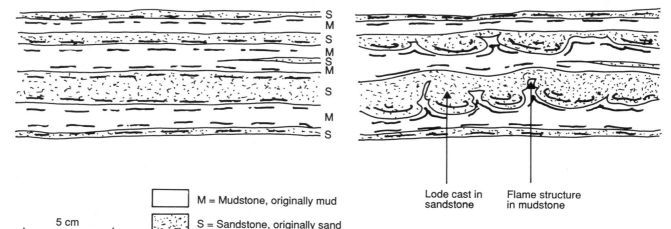

S
M
S
M
S
M

S

M

S

| | M = Mudstone, originally mud |
| | S = Sandstone, originally sand |

5 cm

Lode cast in sandstone

Flame structure in mudstone

Rarely is a complete Bouma sequence developed in one place. Usually only the divisions from the bottom of the sequence or the divisions from the top of the sequence are found. This is because the coarser sediments are deposited near the source of the turbidity current, producing thick deposits, whereas the finer materials are carried further to produce thinner deposits of, for example, alternating D and E divisions, as shown in Figure 3.15. Thus thick, massive turbidite deposits develop near the source, i.e. near the continental slope, probably as part of a submarine fan. Thin turbidites comprising only the upper Bouma divisions are deposited far out on the ocean floor.

Fauna and flora
Due to the catastrophic nature of turbidity currents, organisms are rare and cannot be preserved in living positions. The fact that tracks and trails of some organisms are preserved as sole structures shows that life did exist on the ocean floor, before the turbidity current influx. Some of the feeding traces preserved are found only associated with ancient deep sea environments and thus are good indicators of deep sea deposition in preserved sedimentary sequences (see Figure 3.20, page 100). Other organisms associated with turbidites have all been swept in from shelf areas and are generally rare, although plant debris can be fairly common in turbidite sequences formed off deltas.

Geometry of the sediment body
Turbidity current deposits usually begin in fans which have the geometry shown in Figure 3.9 (page 89). Individual turbidites show great lateral continuity and thus illustrate the stratigraphic principle of Lateral Continuity very well. Turbidite sequences are also very extensive and may be very thick. The top of the sequence is flat, but the bottom may be very irregular, as is shown in Figure 3.16, because the turbidites fill in and smooth out any rugged topography that originally existed on the deep ocean floor. This is why the abyssal plains that floor most of our oceans are so flat. Many deep sea trenches are also filled or partially-filled by turbidites.

Resultant sequence
Thick turbidity current deposits develop where there is great sediment input into an oceanic margin area. The result is that turbidity current deposits tend to build up and

Figure 3.15
The changes in turbidity current deposits away from the source area.
How might the changes in sole structures down current be explained?

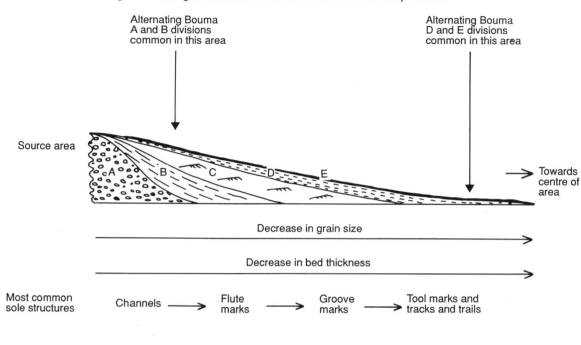

Figure 3.16
A seismic profile across part of the Madeira Abyssal Plain showing how turbidites can flood and smooth out ocean floor topography. (After Heezen and Hollister, 1971; in Reading, 1978.)
What evidence is there that the majority of the ocean floor sediments shown in this profile were deposited by turbidity currents, rather than being pelagic sediments which were deposited by settling from the ocean waters?

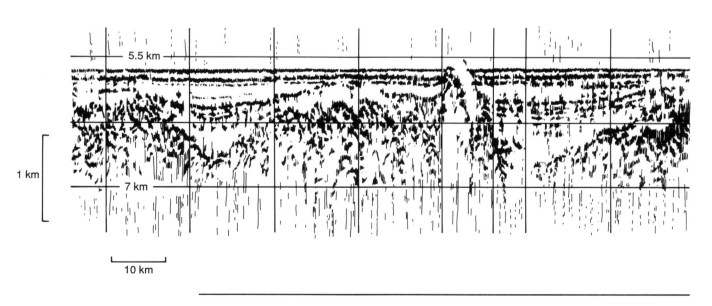

out over older deposits, in much the same way as do many of the other sediment bodies considered, such as deltas. The resultant sequences may therefore begin with pelagic shale deposits, followed by thin turbidites containing only the upper parts of the Bouma sequence because they were deposited far from the source. Further up the sequence the deposits become thicker and thicker and more of the Bouma sequence is found until eventually, thick deposits of Bouma A and B divisions are developed. These probably formed part of the submarine fan, and if so, they will contain distributary channel deposits. The result, therefore is a thick and very extensive coarsening-upward sequence containing all the characteristics of turbidites.

Examples in the British Isles

A sequence such as this has developed in the middle Carboniferous sediments of Derbyshire, and is shown in Figure 3.17. The basin in which the deposit developed was not a deep ocean basin, but, nevertheless, the sequence illustrates well the characteristics described for turbidite/submarine fan sequences. In this case, the delta which provided the sediment for the submarine fan and the turbidites built out over the top of the sequence to produce a second coarsening-upward deposit, capped with coal deposits.

Figure 3.17
A summary stratigraphic log through the succession in the middle Carboniferous Central Pennine Basin. (After Collinson, 1966; Reading, 1964; and Walker, 1966; in Selley, 1970 and Anderton, Bridges, Leeder and Sellwood, 1979.) (Refer to the key given in Figure 1.8 on page 13.)
In this small diagram it is impossible to show the sedimentary structures that are found in the Mam Tor Sandstone beds. Which structures might be expected in the different parts of each bed?

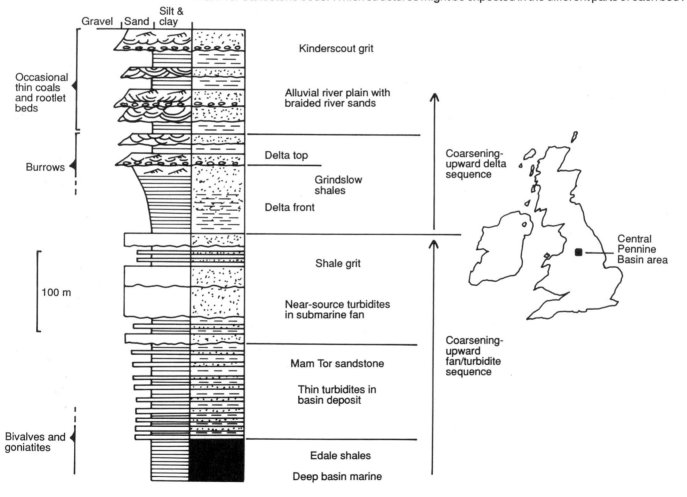

During the middle Cambrian a shelf developed in south-west Wales, with a basin area in central and north Wales. Palaeocurrent measurements show that turbidity current flows moved from the south, northward into the basin, laying down turbidite deposits.

A similar situation occurred during the lower Ordovician when a deep basin developed in the west Wales area off the shelf formed by the Welsh Borderlands region. A thick sequence of turbidites was deposited in the trough. These change from near-source turbidites in the south to thin turbidites that deposited far from the source in the north. The palaeocurrent indicators, such as flute and groove casts, also indicate south to north flow directions for this depositional basin.

Ocean Basins

Ocean basins include the whole region of the ocean floor between the continental slopes on either side. Thus abyssal plains with their rises and deeps, trenches, mid-oceanic ridges and the volcanic piles of seamounts and guyots are all covered by this term. Sedimentation on the ocean floor margins, mainly by turbidity currents, has been dealt with in the previous section. In this section, therefore, we turn our attention to the processes that are active in areas remote from high sediment input, i.e. where sedimentation is slow and the resultant sequences are generally thin.

The study of ocean basins and their sedimentation really began with the voyage of the *Challenger*, between 1872 and 1876. This was the first ever major oceanographic voyage. It carried out dredging for deep-sea sediments in many oceanic areas. On board was the tireless geologist, John Murray, who worked on these sediments. It is on his work that much of our understanding of deep ocean basins is based today. The *Challenger* voyage was followed by voyages of a number of other oceanographic vessels. A big step forward was taken when the *Glomar Challenger* first sailed in 1968. *Glomar Challenger* was the first vessel able to drill deep cores in the ocean basin sediments and these have revealed a wealth of information about deep-sea oceanic processes and sediments of both today and the past. The deep-sea drilling programme continues today with involvement from many countries, including Britain.

Conditions of initiation

The sediments which settle from suspension to the floors of ocean basins are called **pelagic** sediments. Very low energy conditions are necessary for the very fine particles to settle, so accumulations occur well below wave base and the influence of tidal currents. Any pelagic sediments that are deposited near the ocean margins are often so 'diluted' by sediments from the continents that they become unrecognisable. Thus the conditions of initiation for pelagic deposits are ocean depths well below wave base with no great input of clastic materials.

Transportation and deposition of sediments

Transportation and deposition of deep-sea sediments occurs largely by settling from suspension, but in recent years the importance of bottom currents has been recognised. These can be strong enough to erode, transport and deposit sediment, to form current ripples and even, it is thought, to roll over manganese nodules. Erosion by bottom currents accounts for the erosion surfaces and unconformities that have been found in many of the cores from deep-sea drilling. Before the discovery of these bottom currents, which are linked to the world-wide circulation of oceanic waters, the ocean floor was thought by many to be an exceedingly low energy, quiet environment, unruffled by any outside forces.

Calcium carbonate has the unusual property of becoming more soluble at *cooler* temperatures, aragonite being more greatly affected than calcite. Oceans become cooler with depth. The increased solubility of calcium carbonate linked with the overall chemical balance of the oceans means that at certain depths beneath the oceans, the carbonate begins to dissolve. The depth at which this occurs is called the **calcite compensation depth**, and no carbonate sediments are found below this depth. The depth varies within oceans, and from ocean to ocean, roughly between 3 and 5 kilometres. Its depth has also varied in the geological past. This process of calcite dissolution at depth has a great bearing on oceanic sedimentation, and was first recognised by John Murray from his work on the *Challenger*. It explains why relatively thick deep-sea carbonate sediments can be found on ocean ridges and rises, whilst very little carbonate is present on the adjacent ocean floors.

Sediment types

The major sediments found on the deep ocean floors, together with their distribution, are shown in simplified form on the world map, Figure 3.18. The ocean margin sediments are those described in the previous section. The glacial sediments have been deposited on the margins of the major ice caps by melting ice. In places they contain **dropstones**, which are glacial erratics that have been 'rafted' out by icebergs before being dropped to the deep ocean floor.

Figure 3.18
A simplified map of the global distribution of ocean basin sediments. (After Davies and Gorsline, 1976; in Reading, 1978.)
How might the distributions of the ocean margin, glacial and carbonate sediments be explained?

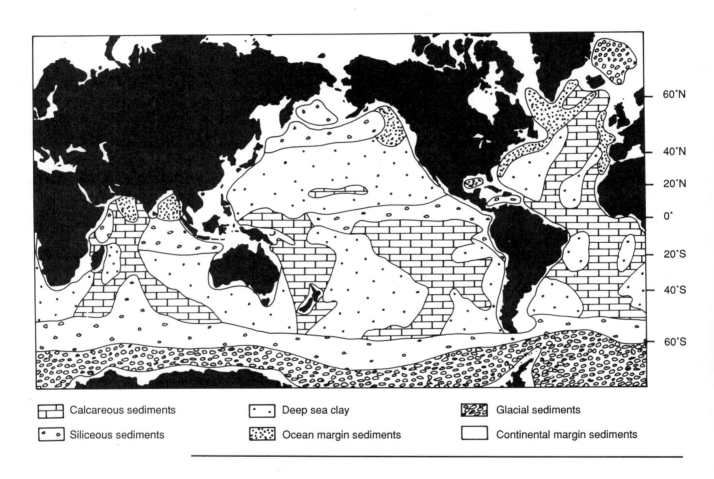

Calcareous sediments	Deep sea clay	Glacial sediments
Siliceous sediments	Ocean margin sediments	Continental margin sediments

The map shows that much of the oceanic basin area is covered by **deep sea clay**. If you had wondered where the finest red sediment winnowed from deserts ended up, here is your answer. The deep sea clay is usually red or brown and contains clay minerals and other very fine-grained minerals, such as quartz, that derived originally from the continents. Much of this dust fell out of suspension in the air to the surface of the sea and then settled gently to the sea bed, although some is simply the suspended sediment in sea water which is unable to settle out in the higher-energy conditions of the continental shelf. The deep-sea clay also contains fine-grained volcanic ash, particularly near active explosive volcanic areas. Small round spherules of cosmic dust that originate beyond our planet are also common in places.

Most of the remaining deep sea sediments are biological in origin. The largest accumulations of these occur beneath areas on the ocean surface where food is provided by upwelling currents rich in dissolved ions. Where food is abundant in the surface waters, the micro-organisms that make up plankton bloom, producing, on death, the sediment that rains down to the sea floor. The settling sediment is either the remains of the organisms themselves or faecal pellets produced by larger organisms. These fine-grained biological accumulations are called **oozes** and are often named after the most abundant organisms in them. **Globigerina ooze** is composed mainly of the shells of planktonic foraminifera, especially *Globigerina* (see Figure 3.19), which are largely composed of calcite. **Pteropod oozes** are made largely of the aragonite

Figure 3.19
Organic components of ocean floor oozes.
Some of these have adaptations for a pelagic mode of life (i.e. for floating near the surface of the ocean) whilst others, apparently, do not. Why should this be so?

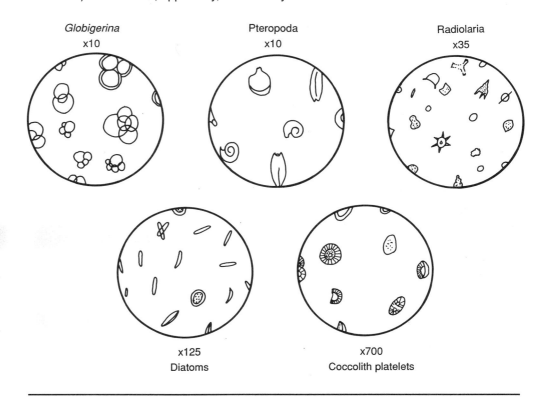

shells of pteropods, which are microscopic gastropods. **Radiolarian ooze** is rich in the siliceous shells of the single-celled radiolarian animals, whilst **diatom ooze** consists mainly of the siliceous cell walls of diatoms, which are microscopic algae. Other algae produce coccoliths. These are small calcite platelets formed in the cell walls and are common components of other types of ooze. Coccolith platelets were of great importance in the formation of the widespread Cretaceous Chalk. Calcareous oozes do not accumulate below the calcite compensation depth because the carbonate dissolves in the sea water and is carried away.

Chemical changes are also important in the formation of **manganese nodules**. These are rounded lumps, from a few millimetres to several centimetres across, that have grown by the precipitation of material rich in manganese and iron from sea water. Their unsteady growth can be seen in the concentric ring structure they develop, like tree rings. These nodules grow extremely slowly – perhaps as little as 3 millimetres in a million years in areas where sedimentation rates are low. At the moment it is too expensive to mine manganese nodules from the deep ocean for manganese and for the nickel, cobalt and copper they also contain. However, with new technologies and rising world prices, it may become economically viable to do so in the future.

Sedimentary structures

The major sedimentary structure found in deep sea sediments is lamination. Some coarser materials contain the cross lamination produced by ripples. In places, bioturbation is fairly extensive.

Fauna and flora

Most of the organisms found in these sediments are a pelagic fauna and flora from near the surface of the sea. Having dropped away from the active upper zones of the sea, their preservation potential is very good, so many of the organisms can become beautifully preserved as fossils. There is also life on the ocean floors, as is shown by the traces left by feeding and burrowing animals. Indeed, some of these traces, such as those shown in Figure 3.20, are characteristic of ancient deep-sea environments, including ocean margin and ocean basin sediments. Thus, preserved mudstones containing traces of these types must be of deep-sea origin rather than, for example, of tidal flat or shallow sea origin.

Figure 3.20
Trace fossils produced by some deep sea organisms. (From Collinson and Thompson, 1982.)
Deep sea feeding trails like these usually have a regular pattern, unlike the feeding trails of many shallow sea organisms. Why is there this difference?

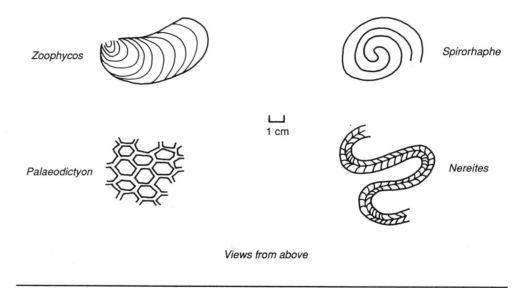

Zoophycos

Spirorhaphe

1 cm

Palaeodictyon

Nereites

Views from above

Geometry of the sediment body

The geometry of deep-sea sediments is of sequences which blanket any topographic changes on the ocean floor. These sediment blankets can be thick. They generally thin towards ocean ridges, where there is 'newer' ocean floor which has not been available for sediment deposition for very long.

Resultant sequence

Resultant sequences show no general characteristic changes from bottom to top, but are characterised by very fine-grained materials which are carbonate-, silica- or clay-rich. These are laminated and sometimes contain the tracks and trails of deep-sea organisms. During diagenesis, silicia-rich deposits often develop chert banding.

Examples in the British Isles

The upper Cambrian black shales and cherts in the Southern Uplands of Scotland are considered to be of deep-sea origin, as are some of the black shales that were deposited during the Ordovician and Silurian in Britain including the Silurian graptolite-rich mudstones of Cumbria.

Another example of deep-sea sedimentation formed during the Devonian in south-west England. At this time there was a shoreline across the area, and the deep sea sediments accumulated in the deep waters south of this shoreline.

Probably the most extensive fine-grained deposit of pelagic origin in the world is the upper Cretaceous Chalk. Chalk now outcrops over many areas of eastern and southern England and forms the white cliffs that are found along several coastlines. There is evidence to suggest that the Chalk Sea may once have covered the whole of the British Isles, forming widespread chalk deposits which have since been eroded away. The origin of the Chalk was a matter of great debate amongst geologists until the scanning electron microscope became available. This showed that the Chalk is composed largely of minute coccolith platelets that must have come from a great algal bloom that affected the seas at this time. Flint nodules are common throughout the Chalk. They are composed of micro-crystalline silica and formed during the diagenesis of the Chalk, when siliceous microfossils and sponges were dissolved and the flint precipitated. There are some indications that the Chalk Sea was not particularly deep. It was certainly extremely quiet to allow the very fine-grained coccolith remains to settle out of suspension.

Confined Basins

In confined basins that form in arid conditions, evaporites precipitate, as described on page 65. In non-arid conditions, euxinic (de-oxygenated) black sediments are often deposited.

The Black Sea is the best example of a large-scale confined basin that exists on Earth today. Euxinic sediments have been deposited there – indeed, the term euxinic comes from the Greek name for the Black Sea. The Black Sea is almost entirely enclosed and is of oceanic depths. It has one small opening with a sill that connects it to the Mediterranean Sea. This small opening has restricted the flow of water, so the waters have become stratified (layered); the circulating surface waters contain normal amounts of oxygen, but the more dense bottom waters have become stagnant. The stagnant bottom waters of the Black Sea extend from a depth of about 150 metres to the bottom, i.e. about 2200 metres down. As is shown in Figure 3.21, these waters contain no oxygen, but they do contain large quantities of dissolved hydrogen sulphide (H_2S). This is a strongly reducing environment and black iron sulphides are deposited in the sediments. Often pyrite (FeS_2) is precipitated too. At times in the recent geological past these conditions have produced black layers of **sapropel**, which is an organic-rich layer deposited under reducing conditions. Sapropels become the **oil shales** preserved in the geological record. These are one of the source rocks of oil.

Such confined basins have occurred on a number of scales in the geological past, with whole areas of oceans sometimes becoming euxinic. In some cases of water stratification in oceans it was not the bottom water that became stagnant, but a layer of water at intermediate depths, so carbon-rich sediments such as sapropels were deposited on ocean margins and on ocean rises, rather than on the ocean floor.

Confined conditions also occurred in shelf environments during the lower Jurassic in southern Britain. (These were discussed in the section on shallow seas, on page 86.) Similar conditions prevailed there for periods of the upper Jurassic as well. Within the sediment sequence, *normal*, *restricted* (i.e. containing a restricted fauna due to lack of oxygen) and *bituminous* mud facies are recognised. The bituminous facies is rich in organic carbon and is very rarely burrowed, thus indicating that the bottom conditions were hostile to life. During their later burial, the bituminous mud facies that were created acted as ideal source rocks for hydrocarbons.

Figure 3.21

A diagrammatic cross-section of the Black Sea to show changes in dissolved oxygen and hydrogen sulphide content. (Based on Theide and van Andel, 1977; in Leeder, 1982.)
This diagram has been drawn with great vertical exaggeration; in reality, the sea floor on the margin of the Black Sea shallows fairly gently. How would you expect the living community, and the traces it produces, to change down this shelving shoreline?

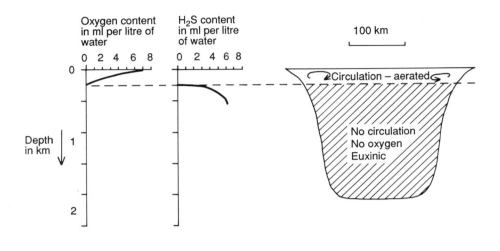

Recognising Offshore Sediments

Key features for the recognition of shallow sea sediments are the presence of the green authigenic mineral glauconite, or an assemblage of trace fossils, like those shown in Figure 3.5 (see page 86). Apart from these two characteristics, shallow sea sediments are similar in many respects to sediments deposited in other environments. Overall there is a tendency towards good sorting and fairly abundant and varied life, with its related fossils and traces.

Turbidite sequences are characteristic of ocean margin environments since turbidite sediments are rarely laid down in other sedimentary environments. The thick sequences of turbidites commonly found in the geological record can only have developed in deep basins.

Trace fossils are important in the recognition of deep sea sediments, and those shown in Figure 3.20 (page 100) are particularly useful in this respect. If such trace fossils are absent, it is often very difficult to determine whether fine-grained sequences were deposited in deep oceans or in very quiet conditions that were much shallower. A sequence that does not contain wave-formed structures could have been deposited either beyond or beneath the influence of waves. If it was deposited beneath wave influence, then the depth could have been anything between 200 and 10,000 metres, there being no features, other than possible trace fossils, by which to determine the depth with any precision. This is why there is still disagreement amongst some geologists about the depth at which some fine-grained sequences, such as the Cretaceous Chalk, were deposited.

Economic Aspects

Oil Source Rocks

Oil is formed by the breakdown of organic material as the temperature of the sediment increases during diagenesis. (This process is described in more detail on page 80 of *Sedimentology Book 1*). The oil then migrates away from the source sediments. If it becomes trapped, it may form an oilfield suitable for exploitation. The oil originates from the organic material found in sapropels and oil shales which form in the way described on page 101. Much of the organic matter in oil shales is unrecognisable in terms of the original organisms, but since the remains of algae and algal spores are common, most of it is thought to be of algal origin, i.e. to be composed of the plant materials of marine plankton. Many oil shales, as well as the modern sediments of the Black Sea, contain a distinct sequence of alternating thin organic and clastic layers. These may well have been caused by annual blooms of algae followed by seasons when the algae were not as prolific.

When more of the world's resources of oil have become exhausted, the price will rise and it may then become economic to recover oil directly from surface outcrops of oil shales, such as the Carboniferous oil shales found in the Midland Valley of Scotland.

Oil shales do not provide the only oil source rocks. Provided that it was thick enough, any fine-grained mud which contained reasonable volumes of organic algal material distributed though it may have been an important oil source.

Hydrocarbons in Submarine Fans and Turbidite Deposits

Ancient deep sea sands have contained highly productive oil and gas accumulations on occasion. It is thought that pelagic deep-sea muds may act as source rocks and that the hydrocarbons migrate upslope into the turbidite sands. There they may be sealed by impermeable mud layers or may become trapped in folds that form later. Some of the lower Tertiary oilfields in the North Sea, including Forties and Montrose, occur in deep sea sands.

Brick Clay

Bricks have been made in the past from a wide variety of clays including upper Carboniferous Coal Measure clays, Triassic lake clays, and even Pleistocene glacial boulder clays (tills). However the best sort of clay for the types of bricks that the building industry requires today are thick, widespread and uniform deposits with a fairly low water content (17–19 per cent). The low water content is important so that there is not much shrinkage of the bricks during drying. Small amounts of calcium carbonate and silt increase strength and reduce shrinkage. If the clay contains organic matter, this releases energy when burned and thus reduces fuel costs during firing. These requirements are best met in Britain by the upper Jurassic Oxford Clay that was deposited in quiet, fairly shallow sea conditions over much of southern and eastern England. Many brickworks are situated on the Oxford Clay, but some of the best known are around Peterborough. Bricks are still made in Britain from a number of other clays, but the Jurassic, lower Cretaceous and Tertiary clays are the most important.

The 'Earths': Fuller's Earth and Diatomaceous Earth

Fuller's Earth is a greenish-brown clay composed mainly of the clay mineral **montmorillonite**. Montmorillonite has great powers of absorbency, and its use for fulling, i.e. cleansing woollen cloth of grease and oil, has given the material its British name of Fuller's Earth. In the United States it is called bentonite. The main use of these montmorillonite-rich clays today is in the oil industry, where they are added to drilling muds to control their viscosity by absorbing water. When pumped up the borehole the drilling muds must be viscous enough to carry the rock chippings from the drill head to the surface. If the mud is allowed to become too viscous, however, the drill can stick in the borehole, which can cause expensive damage. It is the job of mud engineers on drilling platforms to monitor and control mud consistency. Fuller's Earth is also used to clarify wines and beers. Another use is in the manufacture of cat litter, where its mopping-up properties are vital!

Fuller's Earth is exploited in Britain from the middle Jurassic clays of the Bath area in Avon, and from lower Cretaceous clays in southern England. Both these deposits are thought to have formed from volcanic ash that settled into quiet sea conditions, forming volcanic clays.

Diatomaceous earth, or diatomite, is diatom ooze that has become preserved on land. The diatoms are siliceous and extremely small, such that 1 cubic centimetre of diatomaceous earth contains more than 3 million diatoms. Being formed of silica, diatomaceous earth is chemically unreactive and is also very porous. These properties give it its main uses: as a filtering agent, an insulator, and a filler in paints, etc. It is also used as a mild abrasive in metal polishes and as a friction agent on matchboxes. In the past it was extracted on the Isle of Skye for use in the explosives industry.

Diatom ooze accumulates in quiet conditions in deep seas, and also in lakes when blooms of diatom algae occur. Today, the only commercial deposit of diatomaceous earth in Britain comes from post-glacial lakes in northern Cumbria. In other parts of the world, however, important marine and fresh water deposits exist.

Practical Investigation and Fieldwork

1. How do density currents work?
Fill a plastic or glass fish tank two-thirds full of water. In a beaker, mix water with table salt to make a saline solution. Add to this a few crystals of potassium permanganate to dye the saline solution purple and stir. (Be careful: potassium permanganate stains wet fingers.) Whilst observing the tank from the side, with your eyes at the level of its base, pour the saline solution quickly down the inside of one end of the tank. When all the action has ceased, stir the tank and repeat the experiment several times. Draw diagrams to show the shapes of the currents generated, both in cross-section and in plan view. Measure their height and velocity. What controls the velocity of the current? Why doesn't it mix with the rest of the water straight away? What happens to the current when it reaches the other end of the tank? What are the effects of gently tilting the tank in either direction? Investigate the differences caused by different concentrations of salt solution, including one run with no salt at all. Investigate the differences produced by currents containing suspended material, such as milk or muddy water. Which of the density currents you have produced are true turbidity currents?

2. Do density currents work without pouring?
In the density current experiments in the fish tank (Investigation 1), one of the forces driving the current was gravity, since momentum was given to the current by gravity as it was poured down the side of the tank. The effects of pouring can be avoided by adding a gate at one end of the fish tank or by building a density current tank with a gate, as shown in Figure 3.22. When the tank is complete, repeat the experiments described in Investigation 1 above. In this case, the coloured liquid is added to the small area of the tank behind the gate as water is added to the rest of the tank to keep the levels in the gate and the tank the same. The current is generated by swiftly raising the gate. What is the force driving the current in this case? A long density current tank will give you scope for careful measurements of current velocities, which can then be related to different concentrations and different types of fluid.

3. How do graded beds formed in different ways compare with one another?
Take two tall coffee jars or two 250 millilitre measuring cylinders and fill them nearly to the top with water. Add a measure (such as a quarter of a cupful) of mixed sediment (e.g. dry soil mixed with some sand) to each of the two containers and observe carefully. After settling, a graded bed (which changes in grain size from coarser at the base to finer at the top) should be produced in each container. Now take one of the containers and, sealing the top (either with the coffee jar lid or with your hand) shake the container fairly vigorously round and round until the sediment is swirling around the bottom. Then put the container down and observe the deposition of the sediment.

Figure 3.22
A tank suitable for experimenting with density currents.
Longer tanks are preferable to shorter ones for many experiments. Why?

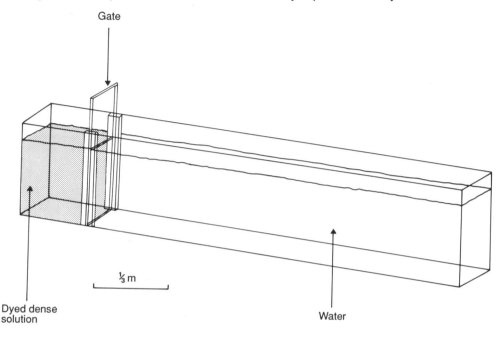

Gate

⅓ m

Dyed dense
solution

Water

A graded bed is again formed. How do the beds in the two jars differ? How do the two processes differ? What controls the order of deposition of the different sizes of particle? Which of the processes is active in turbidity currents and which in the deposition of volcanic ash in quiet water?

Test Your Understanding

1. At the western end of the English Channel, south of Cornwall, many sand waves have been formed by tidal current action. As a result of tidal ebb and flow, all the sand waves are advancing towards the south-west, in the direction of the edge of the continental shelf. Why should this be?

2. Figure 3.23 shows the variation from south to north of the sediments deposited during the lower Jurassic in the region of present-day Bristol. What could be the explanation for these variations?

3. In 1936 the Hoover Dam was built across the Colorado River in southern Nevada, USA. As a consequence, the river valley flooded for many kilometres upstream, forming Lake Mead. From time to time the engineers have noted muddy waters at the foot of the dam beneath clear waters above. How might this mud suspension have been produced?

4. In recent years, side-scan sonar (a type of radar) records have revealed meandering channels on the deep-sea floor. One example is the strongly meandering channel on the deep sea cone of sediments off the River Amazon in Brazil, in 3.5 kilometres of water. Some of the channels have levées on their margins. How might such channels form?

Figure 3.23
Sediment sequences that were laid down during the same time interval in the lower Jurassic of the Bristol area. (From Kellaway and Welch, 1948.)
How could the shale-limestone alternations found at Sparkford and Sodbury be caused?

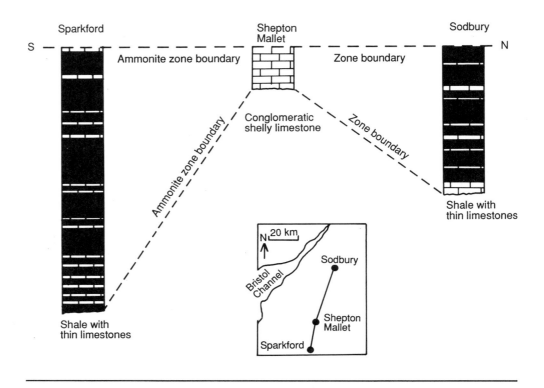

5. Figure 3.24. shows palaeocurrent data measured from the middle and upper Cambrian sandstones in North Wales. How were the channels and sole structures produced? What does the data indicate about the shape of the basin of deposition during the middle and upper Cambrian?

6. At the same time as the sediments in Question 5 were being deposited in North Wales, the middle Cambrian sediments that were being laid down in south-west Wales were as shown in Figure 3.25. What was the type of depositional environment in South Wales at this time? How does this information relate to Figure 3.24 and your answers to Question 5?

7. On an ocean floor containing a mid-oceanic ridge, abyssal plains with deeps and rises, guyots and seamounts, and trenches, where would you expect to find major deposits of the following sediments: calcareous oozes; siliceous oozes; turbidites? Explain your answers. Under what circumstances might interlayered sediments of two different types form?

8. The upper Jurassic Kimmeridge Clay, where it is exposed in cliffs at Kimmeridge on the Dorset coast, contains a layer of bituminous shale. This oil shale is usually less than a metre in thickness. Crinoid fossils found in the shale are always preserved in pyrite. The shale burns readily and it has therefore become known locally as the Kimmeridge Coal. In 1826, spontaneous ignition of the shale gave rise to a fire that burned for four years, at a place now called Burning Cliff. Under what conditions did the bituminous shale accumulate, and why should the fossils it contains have become replaced by pyrite?

Figure 3.24
Palaeocurrent data plotted for the middle Cambrian of North Wales. (From Crimes, 1970; in Anderton, Bridges, Leeder and Sellwood, 1979.)
Why is the rose diagram plotted for channel data near Barmouth symmetrical, whilst the rest of the data plotted for sole structures is not?

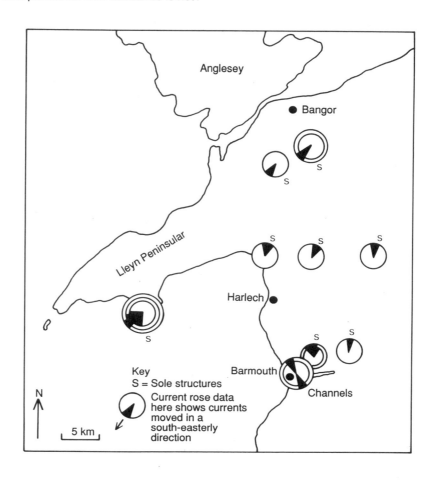

Figure 3.25
A greatly simplified stratigraphic log of the sediments deposited in south-west Wales during the Cambrian. (Based on Anderton, Bridges, Leeder and Sellwood, 1979.) (Refer to the key given in Figure 1.8 on page 13.)
Why are the Lingulella fossils likely to be well preserved?

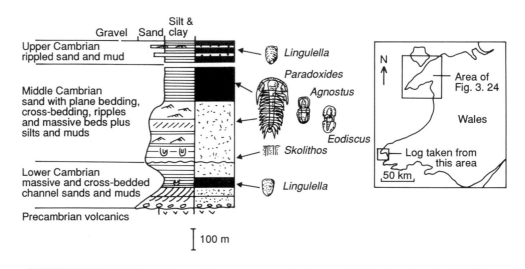

4. WHAT DOES THE SEQUENCE OF ANCIENT ENVIRONMENTS MEAN?

Figure 0.1 (pages 2–3) shows a sequence of ancient environments in the British Isles. It is far from complete: the examples it contains are only the ones that have been used in the previous chapters. They were chosen as they illustrate particularly well ancient sequences which have been interpreted in terms of modern sedimentary processes. Many other examples could have been chosen from different parts of the geological column or from different parts of the country. Nevertheless, this partial geological history does show a number of general points about the development, since the late Precambrian (i.e. over the last 1,000 million years or so), of the area that is now the British Isles.

By reading the table from the bottom to the top, you will notice that the depth of the area has been very variable. For example the Scottish Torridonian sequence, formed on land, was followed by the Dalradian shelf sea deposits and then the Cambrian deep sea deposits of the Southern Uplands. In fact the whole of the British Isles area has shown tremendous fluctuations in depth/height. Areas that were seas have become mountains and areas that were mountains have become seas.

A second change that has occurred in the British Isles over this period is a change in climate, as is shown in Figure 4.1. Shelf carbonates were being deposited during the Silurian in conditions that today are found only in or near the tropics. Later, Devonian meandering streams laid down deposits in hot, fairly arid conditions. This was followed by the tropical coal swamps of the Carboniferous, then a return to hot, arid conditions during the Permian and Triassic. The hot environments continued until the Tertiary, which ended with the cooling linked to the onset of the Quaternary ice ages. The final climate (so far ...) is the temperate one we know today. How can this climatic sequence be explained?

First, the effect of the ice ages must be removed from considerations of general trends. Ice ages are unusual events in the history of the Earth. Only five major ice ages have been recorded in the whole geological column. We do not know how ice ages are triggered, but when they occur, the effects of the ice and the cooling of the Earth are felt far beyond the polar areas where they are found today.

Ignoring the ice-age anomaly therefore, what overall trend is shown? It is a change from warm, to hot and arid, to tropical, to hot and arid, warm, to cool. Before the 1960s, these changes were extremely difficult to explain. However, we now understand this climatic sequence in terms of plate tectonics.

The plate tectonic interpretation is that the area that is now Britain was south of the equator (at roughly latitude 30° S) in the Cambrian. During the hot, semi-arid Devonian, it was at the latitude of the southern hemisphere deserts of today (e.g. the Great Australian Desert). During the Carboniferous, the tropical conditions were, we think, equatorial conditions, as the area was on the equator. This was followed by desert

Figure 4.1
The movement of the British Isles through geological time, based on climatic evidence and a variety of other types of evidence. The latitudes are very approximate. (The dates are taken from Snelling, 1985.)
Some of the evidence used has been fossil evidence. How can fossil types and communities give information on ancient climatic conditions?

Geological era	Geological period/system	Time m.y.	General climatic conditions	Approximate latitude of British Isles
	Today	0	Cool temperate	50–60° N
Cenozoic	Quaternary	1.8	Varying from glacial to sub-tropical	50–60° N
	Tertiary	65	Sub-tropical (e.g. Mediterranean)	35–50° N
	Cretaceous	135	Sub-tropical	30–45° N
Mesozoic	Jurassic	205	Sub-tropical (e.g. Bahamas)	28–40° N
	Triassic	250	Sub-tropical, arid (e.g. Sahara)	8–40° N
	Permian	290	Sub-tropical to tropical, arid	5° S–20° N
(upper)	Carboniferous	355	Tropical (equatorial)	8° S–10° N
	Devonian	405	Sub-tropical, semi-arid (e.g. Kalahari)	30°–8° S
Palaeozoic	Silurian	435	Warm	30–20° S
(lower)	Ordovician	510	Warm	30–20° S
	Cambrian	570	Warm	30–20° S
	Precambrian	4,600	Variable?	

N.B. The examples given in this table are of comparable environments on Earth today.

conditions again as the region passed through the zone of present-day northern hemisphere deserts, such as the Sahara. Following this there was a very gradual cooling as the area which is now Britain moved northwards to its present position in the temperate zone. This movement of our area through the climatic regions of the Earth is plotted on Figure 4.2. It is very good evidence for the movement of continents during geological time and therefore for the overall theory of plate tectonics.

Figure 4.2
The general northward movement of the British Isles area through the different climatic regions of the Earth since the Cambrian (any variation in longitude is not known and so is not plotted). Why is movement of the continent carrying the area now Britain a more likely explanation than movement of the climatic regions?

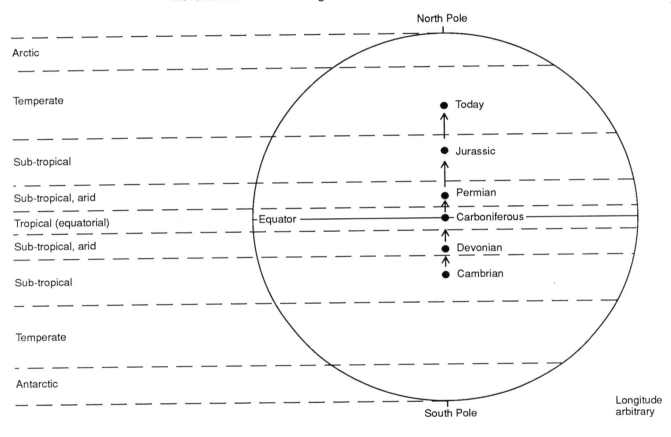

This fairly steady northward movement of the area we now call the British Isles has thus been part of the world-wide plate tectonic movements that have affected Earth since the Precambrian. The movements are caused by **convection currents** in the partially molten rock in part of the upper mantel. Where the Earth's heat flow is high, the currents rise and flow outward from the 'hot spots' towards cooler areas where they sink and then return to their origins, thus forming a convection cell of mobile mantle material. The upper, outward flowing currents carry the sheets of solid **lithosphere** we now call **plates.** The solid lithosphere is made up of the solid extreme outer part of the mantle together with the Earth's crust.

Many of the Earth's plates carry continents; Britain's northward movement has been as part of the continental material that has been carried 'on the backs' of plates. When convection cells carry two plates towards each other, they collide. Britain has been involved in major plate collisions at least three times in the geological past. When plates collide tremendous **tectonic** forces (i.e. pressures within the Earth) are produced, resulting in the formation of high mountain ranges as the existing rocks become crumpled and broken. This is one of the causes of the 'rise and fall' of Britain over this period. At times of steady plate movement, much of the area has been covered by sea, producing marine depositional conditions. The collisions have forced the area above sea level so that continental conditions follow (i.e. erosion and deposition on the land surface). Major changes from marine to continental conditions are thus good evidence for plate collisions.

However, such changes can also be caused by world-wide (eustatic) changes in sea level. During the glaciations great changes in sea level occurred because when much of the world's water was locked up as ice on the land, there was less available to fill the oceans which were therefore much lower. When the great ice caps were melted by natural global warming, sea level became much higher. Since glaciations are rare events in the Earth's history, eustatic changes caused by them have been equally rare.

There have also been major eustatic changes *between* the glaciations, as is shown in Figure 4.3. The diagram shows that sea levels were highest during the Ordovician and the Cretaceous periods. They were lowest during the early Cambrian, the Triassic to early Jurassic period, and today. These changes were caused by differences in the volume of the ocean basins that are probably linked to plate tectonics. It is thought that when a new rising convection current heats the lithosphere, this moves upwards since it is less dense. If this heating and rising of the lithosphere occurs in an ocean basin, the ocean waters are displaced and these then rise and flood onto low-lying areas of the

Figure 4.3
The variation of sea level on Earth since the Cambrian. (Data taken from Harland, Cox, Llewellyn, Pickton, Smith and Walters, 1982.)
What evidence preserved in the rock sequence shows how sea levels have changed?

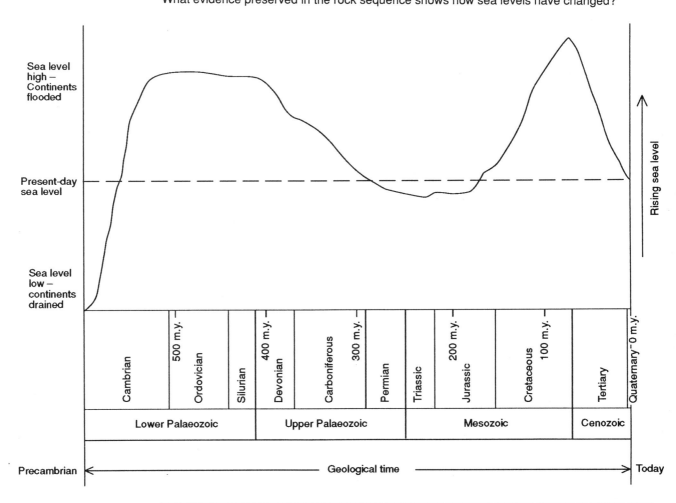

continents. The opposite occurs when a rising convection current fades away. Then the lithosphere above it cools and slowly sinks, allowing the ocean waters back into the basin. World-wide sea levels then fall and the seas covering part of continents become shallower or drain away all together to form land again.

This picture of rising and falling sea level has been fossilised as a sequence of environments in the rocks. Sea levels can rise to flood vast areas of the Earth's continents, or fall to leave much of the continents exposed. These movements are caused naturally either by plate tectonics or by glaciations. During the glaciations, sea levels changed very quickly, in terms of geological time, and so these rapid changes cannot be seen on a generalised curve of sea level changes like the one in Figure 4.2.

If large-scale global warming occurs today, it will certainly cause seas to flood low-lying areas, as has happened in the past. However, it is very difficult to predict whether short-term changes in global climate are part of a longer term warming. It is even more difficult to find out if any long-term warming is natural global warming or a greenhouse effect produced by our own activities world-wide.

Whatever happens in the future, we can be sure that rises and falls in sea level and future changes in the climate of Britain will be preserved in the sequences of sedimentary environments fossilised in the rock record.

Further Reading

Allen, J. R. L., *Physical Processes of Sedimentation*, Allen and Unwin, 1970.

Allen, J. R. L., *Experiments in Physical Sedimentology*, Allen and Unwin 1985a.

Allen, J. R. L., *Principles of Physical Sedimentology*, Allen and Unwin, 1985b.

Anderton, R., Bridges, P. H., Leeder, M. R., and Sellwood, B. W., *A Dynamic Stratigraphy of the British Isles*, Allen and Unwin, 1979.

Collinson, J. D., and Thompson, D. B., *Sedimentary Structures*, Allen and Unwin, 1982.

Harland, W. B., Cox, A. V., Llewellyn, P. G., Pickton, C. A. G., Smith, A. G. and Walters R., *A Geological Time Scale*, Cambridge University Press, 1982.

Keen, M. J., *An Introduction to Marine Geology*, Pergamon, 1968.

Kellaway, G. A. and Welch, F. B. A., *British Regional Geology – Bristol and Gloucester District*, HMSO, 1948.

Kennett, P., 'A Simulation Experiment of a Palaeoecological Process for Pupils of All Ages', *Geology Teaching*, 8, No.4, 1983.

Kennett, P. and Ross, C. A., *Fossils and Time*, Longman, 1983a.

Kennett, P. and Ross, C. A., *Palaeoecology*, Longman, 1983b.

King, C., 'Experimental Sedimentology using a Motorised Wave Tank', *Geology Teaching*, 5, No. 2, 1980.

King, C., 'Field Excursions to Modern Depositional Environments', *Geology Teaching*, 9, No. 3, 1984.

Leeder, M. R., *Sedimentology – Process and Product*, Allen and Unwin, 1982.

Reading, H. G. (ed.), *Sedimentary Environments and Facies*, Blackwell, 1978.

Reineck, H. E. and Singh, I. B., *Depositional Sedimentary Environments*, Springer-Verlag, 1973.

Selley, R. C., *Ancient Sedimentary Environments*, Chapman and Hall, 1970.

Selley, R. C., *Introduction to Sedimentology*, Academic Press, 1976.

Snelling, N. J. (ed.), 'The Chronology of the Geological Record' Mem. 10. *Geological Society of London*, Blackwell, 1985.

Thompson, D. B., 'Exercises on the Understanding of Trace Fossils', *Geology Teaching*, 11, No. 1, 1986.

Tucker, M. E., *Sedimentary Petrology, An Introduction*, Blackwell, 1981.

Watson, J., *Geology and Man*, Allen and Unwin, 1983.

Whitfield, W. B., 'The Development and Educational Uses of a Motorised Wavetank', *Geology Teaching*, 4, No. 2, 1979.

Also recommended are the following units from the Earth Science Teachers' Association, available from Geo Supplies Ltd, 16 Station Road, Chapeltown, Sheffield S30 4XH.

'*Science of the Earth*' units 1, 4–9, 11–12, 14, 18, 20;

'*Science of the Earth 11–14*' 3-unit packs: 'Sediment on the move', 'Power from the past', 'Secondhand rocks'.

Index

Each term shown in **bold type** in the index is defined on the page whose number is shown in **bold**.